CW00546617

Diversity and Inclusion Unlocked ™ Planner

Diversity and Inclusion Unlocked ™ Planner

Time to unlock opportunities to accelerate your business success

The fact that you're here means you already know something hundreds of thousands of small business owners don't know yet…

You know you need to consider diversity and inclusion in your small business or risk failure.

It's that simple,

There are two compelling reasons:

The Moral case and the Financial case. I'm pretty sure since you're here, I don't need to explain the moral case. You are a human being who wants to be on the right side of history, who cares about the experiences of others and want those experiences to be positive ones too not a tick box or tokenism. I know that already.

But the financial case? Now that is a secret the giant corporates, tech billionaires and high-level entrepreneurs have been in on for a while, and I'm here to let you in on it too!

Businesses that are diverse and inclusive are 25% more likely to outperform their peers in a similar industry! (McKinsey Report 2019)

Yes. 25%. Let that sink in for a sec. In the UK that's tapping into £24 billion. In the US, it's TRILLIONS.

And the thing is, big businesses know this already. They're already investing in experts to consult on diversity and inclusion strategies at the very highest levels of their business.

Experts like me.

But here's the thing: I don't want to be their best-kept secret. I want to arm small business owners just like you with the same knowledge, data and insights, so you can start to make the important changes to your business operations right now, whilst your business is still agile and growing.

That's my mission. As a career and business strategist, my goal is to light the path to creating more diverse and inclusive businesses.

Verna Myers said: "Diversity is being invited to the party; inclusion is being asked to dance."

As a business mum with five children, I want them and others like them to grow up in a world where they are always asked to dance.

Are you ready to join me? You're invited to the party!

See you on the inside*!*

Samantha Lubanzu

"Diversity is a reality. Inclusion is a choice"

Stephen Frost & Raafi-Karim Alidina

Diversity and Inclusion Unlocked ™ Planner

Are you making the right Diversity and Inclusion decisions?

Before you begin your DIversity and Inclusion Unlocked Planning I would like to share my 5 Diversity and Inclusion top tips which you can implement immediately, to improve the diversity and inclusion of your small business.

Because simply put: Diversity is the reality of the world we live in. It's the inclusion that's the choice. So, here are 5 quick and easy steps to making the right choice in the right way to achieve the right results for your business NOW

Step 1. Awareness: Think carefully about the stereotypes you've seen, know about and believe in that may have formed your own unconscious bias and challenge your thinking. Then evaluate your business and check how diversity and inclusion might apply to you.

Ask yourself: What am I doing to help? How am I participating in this conversation? How are people in my audience marginalised and how may I create a sense of belonging?

How could I adapt my business to accommodate my diverse audience and make them feel a sense of belonging and inclusion? How does my diverse audience celebrate festivals and holidays?

The Diversity and Inclusion Unlocked planner is the first step in your Awareness Journey

Step 2. Education: In an ideal world, this would be the first step, but awareness of a problem must come before a willingness to solve it. So, now it's time to go and understand how we got to where we are in terms of diversity and inclusion. I would recommend you educate yourself with books, podcasts and audiobooks. Do not rely on just one source of information.

Why I'm No Longer Talking to White People About Race

Twice As Hard: Navigating Black Stereotypes And Creating Space For Success

Step 3. Understand your legal obligations: Find out about the legal obligations surrounding diversity and inclusion in the country where you live and operate. If you're a global business you'll need to understand the wider picture of legal obligations.

Step 4. Understand your supply chain: How much diversity is there? Who are you buying from and outsourcing to? Who's in your audience? Who's buying your products and services, and who feels comfortable (or not!) in the spaces you create?

Think about how you can reach out to a wider and more diverse audience and create spaces they feel included.

Step 5. Consult the Experts: Find, follow and reach out to experts in the field of diversity and inclusion, and understand from them how you can begin to take action to improve things in your business – experts like me.

Start as you mean to go on With the help of this planner, I will lead you through the first phase of the journey—AWARENESS – in 365-days

ALL THINGS ARE POSSIBLE ...

How to use your Diversity and Inclusion Unlocked Planner

Each Month covers each diversity and inclusion awareness day and explains what the day is, why it is important and the communities it impacts.

1. Choose awareness days that personally resonate with you and your ideal audience

2. Fill in the Diversity and Inclusion Unlocked reflective boxes with important diversity and inclusion actions:

- How can I add value to this community?

- What activities could I plan to support this awareness day?

- How can I show my support on Social Media?

- How can I continue the momentum?

3. Schedule planning time on a daily/weekly basis.

4. Spend time having some fun and get creative with your diversity and inclusion planning

5. Don't forget the hashtag and tag us in too

#DiversityandInclusionUnlocked

Diversity and Inclusion Unlocked ™ Planner

January 2024

Sunday	Monday	Tuesday	Wednesday	Thursday	Friday	Saturday
	1 New Years Day Emancipation Proclamation anniversary (U.S.)	2	3	4 World Braille Day	5 George Washington Carver Day	6 Feast of the Epiphany (Christian)
7	8	9	10	11	12	13 **Lohri Hindu
14	15 Martin Luther King Day (U.S.) **Makar Sankranti (Hindu) Blue Monday	16 National Day of Racial Healing (U.S)	17 **Guru Gobind Singh Birthday Sikh	18	19	20
21 **World Religion Day	22	23	24 International Day of Education	25 **Mahayana New Year (Buddhist)	26	27 International Day of Commemoration in Memory of the Victims of the Holocaust.
28	29	30	31	1	2	3

Slavery and Human Trafficking Prevention Month (U.S.)

**National Mentoring Month

**Awareness Day or Month not included in overview

January

January 1: New Year's Day (An inclusive day for most)

What is it about?

Nothing beats that feeling when the clock hits midnight and everyone screams, Happy New Year!

Goodbye 2022. Welcome 2023.

The end of a year is always a great time but seeing a new year begin is even more special.

That's what makes January 1 significant. It makes a fresh start, a new beginning and a time to improve on the previous year.

Who does it impact?

People in the western world, especially Christians.

Why is it important?

A new year signifies a new beginning, a new dawn and a new era. It is a time to make new year resolutions(even if we forget them by February), pick ourselves up from where we stopped and prepare for the year ahead.

Important hashtags: #NewYear2023 #Newyear #2023

LET'S UNLOCK

How can I add value to this community?

What activities could I plan to support this awareness day?

How can I show my support on social Media?

How can I continue the momentum?

The 3rd Monday in January: Martin Luther King Day (U.S.)

What is it about?

Arrested **29** times. A minister. a civil rights activist and one of the greatest orators of all time. It can only be one man, Dr. Martin Luther King.

King was a civil rights activist and the leader of the peaceful demonstration against the racial discrimination of people. of colour from **1955** till **1968** when he was assassinated.

Every **3**rd Monday of January is marked out to remember his efforts towards civil rights activism for people of colour.

Who does it impact?

People of colour

Why is it important?

We've come a long way as a society in the war against racism. However, there's still work to be done to make racism and discrimination a thing of the past. The first step is talking about the problem.
Racism might be an awkward conversation to have but its absolutely necessary. We must learn our history and the impact racism had, and still has, on individuals and how we can work together collectively to overcome it.

Important hashtags: #MLKDay #MartinLutherKingDay #RememberingMLK, #HappyMLKDay

LET'S UNLOCK

How can I add value to this community?

What activities could I plan to support this awareness day?

How can I show my support on social Media?

How can I continue the momentum?

January (Third Monday of the month): Blue Monday

What is it about?

The temperatures are frigid. The days are short. The atmosphere feels gloomy. Welcome to blue Monday,

January is always a bit slow because you are probably low on cash from all the spending during the holidays.

Historically, Blue Monday was tagged "the most depressing day of the year" due to the gloomy weather, short days and the lows that follow after the highs of the holiday celebrations.

Sometimes these lows take a toll on our mental health and affect our productivity.

That's why blue monday is a time to check up on your mental health and make sure the blues don't get the best of you. So get to work, keep your body moving and get the serotonin rolling to keep the blues away.

Who does it impact?

People who are depressed or perceived to be unhappy.

Why is it important?

After the Christmas and holiday celebrations, the excitement quickly fades in January when we get back to work. Coming down from these massive highs can affect our mental health.

Blue Monday is a time to focus on our mental health of others and give advice on how to stay productive in spite of the unpleasant mood.

Important hashtags: #BlueMonday #Depression

LET'S UNLOCK

How can I add value to this community?

What activities could I plan to support this awareness day?

How can I show my support on social Media?

How can I continue the momentum?

LET'S UNLOCK

How can I add value to this community?

What activities could I plan to support this awareness day?

How can I show my support on social Media?

How can I continue the momentum?

January 27: International Day of Commemoration in Memory of Victims of the Holocaust (United Nations)

What is it about?

Over 6 million Jews were killed by Nazi Germany ruled by Hitler between 1941-1945. January 27 is a rememberance day for victims of this horrible genocide.

Who does it impact?

Jews, Christians, survivors of the holocaust and people of other religions, as well as all other minorities who were victims of Nazi persecution during World War II.

Why is it important?

The amount of Jewish Holocaust survivors is growing rapidly, with an estimated 6 million now alive. The events that transpired during the Holocaust have helped to shape modern society and its history. The International Day of Commemoration allows us to have a moment of reflection and share these stories.

Important hashtags: #HolocaustMemorialDay #HolocaustRemembrance

LET'S UNLOCK

How can I add value to this community?

What activities could I plan to support this awareness day?

How can I show my support on social Media?

How can I continue the momentum?

February 2024

Sunday	Monday	Tuesday	Wednesday	Thursday	Friday	Saturday
28	29	30	31	1 National Freedom Day (U.S.) **World Hijab Day	2	3
4 Black History Month (U.S.) Rosa Parks Day **World Cancer Day	5	6 **Lailat al Miraj (Islam)	7	8	9	10 Chinese New Year (Lunar New Year)
11 **Autism Sunday ((International Day of Women & Girls in science	12 International Epilepsy Day	13 ((Mardi Gras	14 Valentine's Day Frederick Douglass Day (U.S.) Ash Wednesday	15 Nirvana Day (Buddhist)	16	17
18	19	20 ((World Day of Social Justice	21	22	23	24
25	26	27	28	29 **Leap Day	1	2

February: LGBT+ History Month (U.K.)

((February: Race Equality Week - 5-11TH FEBRUARY 2024 (U.K.)

**Awareness Day or Month not included in the overview

Diversity and Inclusion Unlocked ™ Planner

February

February: LGBT+ History Month (U.K.)

What is it about?

The month of February is dedicated to the remembrance of LGBT+ history in the UK. It's a time for a reflection on how far we as a society have progressed in being more inclusive for the LGBT+ community.

Who does it impact?

People from all over the world who are of diverse sexual orientation and/or gender identities. This includes, but not limited to, heterosexuals, bisexuals, homosexuals, transgender people, etc. People may be allies with those who do not receive equal societal support and rights.

Why is it important?

LGBT+ History Month is important to help educate people about the history of the community. It's important because it helps us to understand where we have been, and how far we've come as a community.

Important hashtags: #LGBTHistoryMonth #LGBT #Pride

LET'S UNLOCK

How can I add value to this community?

What activities could I plan to support this awareness day?

How can I show my support on social Media?

How can I continue the momentum?

February 4: Rosa Parks Day

What is it about?

Picture this. You get on a bus. Pay your fare and pick a comfortable seat for yourself. Then suddenly, the driver tells you to vacate your seat for another person because of the colour of your skin. What do you do? This scenario played out in a Montgomery bus in 1943 when Rosa Parks when the bus driver ordered Parks to vacate her seat for other white people when the white section of the bus was full. Parks rejected the driver's order and she was eventually arrested for that.

However, she went on to be honoured by the United Congress as "the first lady of civil rights" and "the mother of the freedom movement" In Missouri and California, February 4 is dedicated to remembering her bravery and efforts towards fighting racial segregation.

Who does it impact?

It is celebrated by people of colour and anyone who values equality, justice, and dignity.

Why is it important?

By encouraging students and staff to become more aware of their own cultural heritage and the diversity of our nation, school districts can build bridges between themselves and other communities.

Important hashtags: #RosaParksDay

LET'S UNLOCK

How can I add value to this community?

What activities could I plan to support this awareness day?

How can I show my support on social Media?

How can I continue the momentum?

February 5: Black History Month (U.S.)

What is it about?

The history of the black race in America is highly significant and it is crucial for all to be knowledgeable about it. It reminds us of the roots, culture, identity and tradition of the black race. Black History Month is a time to celebrate the accomplishments, contributions and history of African Americans.

Who does it impact?

People of colour of all ages

Why is it important?

Now more than ever it is crucial to educate our children and co-workers on the contributions of African Americans. The struggle for racial equality and civil rights is not over, nor has it been achieved. The sacrifices made by previous generations must continue to be recognized and celebrated.

Important hashtags: #BlackHistoryMonth #blacklivesmatter #blm

LET'S UNLOCK

How can I add value to this community?

```


```

What activities could I plan to support this awareness day?

```


```

How can I show my support on social Media?

```


```

How can I continue the momentum?

```


```

February 10: Chinese New Year (Lunar Year)

What is it about?

A new year is always a special time anywhere in the world and it's not different with China. The Chinese new year starts on the first day of the lunar calendar and it is celebrated in colourful and spectacular fashion with firecrackers, red colours and lots of gifts being shared. It's a wonderful time for families to come together and celebrate.

Who does it impact?

South East Asians and the Chinese.

Why is it important?

February 10 is also known as Chinese New Year, and this day is dedicated to celebrating the beginning of the Lunar new year. This celebration begins with a parade in which people pray for good fortune while walking around carrying red lanterns, followed by family feasts.

Important hashtags: #ChineseNewYear

LET'S UNLOCK

How can I add value to this community?

What activities could I plan to support this awareness day?

How can I show my support on social Media?

How can I continue the momentum?

February 14: Valentine's Day

What is it about?

It's that time of the year when couples share gifts, go on dates and show affection to one another like never before. But who says Valentine is for couples only? It's the season of love so it's a time to show love to everyone around you.
February 14 is a day to do something special for those special people in your life. Your parents, siblings, spouse, kids, friends etc.

Who does it impact?

It is a day celebrated by all no matter age, gender, and religious lifestyles

Why is it important?

It's fun to celebrate love and relationships. Also, it is useful to learn to make yourself happy. The celebration of this holiday allows us to do this more openly than other days of the year. It is a good day to help others appreciate themselves and be happy.

Important hashtags: #Iloveyou #ValentinesDay #LoveDay

LET'S UNLOCK

How can I add value to this community?

What activities could I plan to support this awareness day?

How can I show my support on social Media?

How can I continue the momentum?

February 14: Frederick Douglass Day (U.S.)

What is it about?

The early 19th century was a difficult period for people of colour like Frederick Douglass who had to escape slavery to gain freedom and then became a leader of the abolitionist movement. He became more popular for his writings and public speaking against slavery.

Who does it impact?

People of colour.

Why is it important?

This day set a precedent of recognizing the contributions to society of people who are people of colour. There were many people of colour who were contributors to society as a person of colour. And thus, honouring them on their special day, would be a great way to acknowledge and appreciate their contributions.

Important hashtags: #FrederickDouglassDay #BlackLivesMatter #IndigenousLivesMatter

LET'S UNLOCK

How can I add value to this community?

What activities could I plan to support this awareness day?

How can I show my support on social Media?

How can I continue the momentum?

February 15: Nirvana Day (Buddhist)

What is it about?

It is a day to remember the Buddha and to celebrate Buddha's complete achievement of nirvana after the physical death of his body.

Who does it impact?

People of all faiths, especially Buddhists

Why is it important?

The Buddha was a person who dedicated his life to helping all people. His teachings and identity were particularly influential to people of Asian descent. It is a day to remember the life of the Buddha and to appreciate the freedom that we have that he never did.

Important hashtags: #NirvanaDay #BuddhaDay

LET'S UNLOCK

How can I add value to this community?

What activities could I plan to support this awareness day?

How can I show my support on social Media?

How can I continue the momentum?

February 22: Ash Wednesday

What is it about?

A holy day of prayer and fasting. It marks the beginning of Lent which is a time for sober reflection on the life of Jesus and his ultimate sacrifice. This period is for us to think back on the sacrifice Jesus paid for our sins.

Who does it impact?

People of all Christian faiths who observe Ash Wednesday.

Why is it important?

Ash Wednesday helps us remember how worthy we are to God and the ways we can grow in faith. It gives us a chance to repent and renew our commitment to God. The Lenten season has been used as a time to reflect on personal sins, repentance, and the need for a change in behaviour both individually and in society as a whole. Lent is a time to consider: am I holy? Should I be? What would change if I were?

Important hashtags: #AshWednesday #WorldAshWednesday

LET'S UNLOCK

How can I add value to this community?

What activities could I plan to support this awareness day?

How can I show my support on social Media?

How can I continue the momentum?

March 2022

Monday	Tuesday	Wednesday	Thursday	Friday	Saturday	Sunday
26	27	28	29	1 **Zero Discrimination Day ** Employee Appreciation Day (U.S.)	2	3
4	5	6	7	8 International Women's Day (U.K)	9	10 Harriet Tubman Day (U.S.) Ramadan (Islamic)
11	12	13	14	15 **International Day to Combat Islamophobia.	16 Marks Publication of the First Black Newspaper in America	17 St. Patrick's Day (Irish/U.S.)
18	19	20 **Naw-Ruz (Baha'l New Year)	21 International Day for the Elimination of Racial Discrimination World Down Syndrome Day	22	23 Purim	24 Holi Palm Sunday **Holika Dahan (Hindu)
25 National Cerebral Palsy Awareness Day	26 **Epilepsy Awareness Day/ Purple Day	27	28 Maundy Thursday	29 Good Friday	30 World Bipolar Day	31 **International Transgender Day of Visibility Easter Sunday

**Awareness Day or Month not included in the overview

**Developmental Disabilities Awareness Month

((Ethnic Equalities Month   ((Gender Equality Month

March 13-19: Neurodiversity Celebration Week (U.K.)   March 1st to 31st: Women's History Month (weekdays only)

March

March 1st to 31st: Women's History Month (weekdays only)

What is it about?

Over the years, women have made a mark and hit milestones in several aspects of society.

The month of March is dedicated to celebrating and honouring the achievements of women all over the world.

Who does it impact?

Women and girls.

Why is it important?

This day allows us to recognise the contributions and impact women and girls make in society, as well as recognising the oppression, discrimination and inequalities they face.

Important hashtags: #womeninhistory

LET'S UNLOCK

How can I add value to this community?

```



```

What activities could I plan to support this awareness day?

```



```

How can I show my support on social Media?

```



```

How can I continue the momentum?

```



```

March 23: Purim

What is it about?

Purim is a Jewish holiday that is celebrated on the 14th day of the Hebrew month of Adar, which occasionally falls in March. The purpose is to celebrate and remember the story of Esther and how God saved his people from attempted genocide.

Who does it impact?

Jew's who observe Purim

Why is it important?

Purim celebrates the Jewish people's survival and reminds us to be thankful for the lives we have. It also gives us a chance to celebrate our faith, even when times are hard, and shows us that we have strength in numbers.

Important hashtags: #Purim #WorldPurim

LET'S UNLOCK

How can I add value to this community?

What activities could I plan to support this awareness day?

How can I show my support on social Media?

How can I continue the momentum?

March 8: International Women's Day (U.K.)

What is it about?

International Women's Day is the day we give shout outs to our mothers, daughters, sisters, aunties and all women for their political, economic and social achievements.
Throughout history, women have endured discrimination and had to fight for their rights.

On this day, women are to be appreciated for all their efforts and sacrifices. Reach out to a woman today and celebrate her.

Who does it impact?

Women & girls.

Why is it important?

The day's importance is also based on the fact that women and girls were second-class citizens to men in the past, which was demeaning, unfair, and unjust. Therefore, this day was created to recognize their contributions and celebrate their achievements. Although equality has been achieved in many countries today, there are still struggles faced by women and girls across the world.

Important hashtags: #InternationalWomensDay

LET'S UNLOCK

How can I add value to this community?

What activities could I plan to support this awareness day?

How can I show my support on social Media?

How can I continue the momentum?

March 10: Harriet Tubman Day (U.S.)

What is it about?

Born into slavery, Harriet Tubman is popularly for escaping slavery and organising the escape of over 70 others.

March 10 is a day to honour the life and legacy of Harriet Tubman, an African American abolitionist who was born into slavery in the 19th century. She escaped from slavery and became an anti-slave activist.

Who does it impact?

People of colour, women & girls.

Why is it important?

Hariet's resistance against slavery and her ability to free slaves from the south despite having been a slave herself plays a huge part in her legacy. She was able to fight against slavery with the help of other slave owners, which displays her courage and perseverance, and her ability to stand up.

Important hashtags: #HarietTubmanDay

LET'S UNLOCK

How can I add value to this community?

What activities could I plan to support this awareness day?

How can I show my support on social Media?

How can I continue the momentum?

March 13-19: Neurodiversity Celebration Week (U.K.)

What is it about?

It's currently estimated to be about 15% of children with learning differences.
While many get help to overcome their challenge and aid their learning, they are likely to feel frustrated, embarrassed or get bullied.

Neurodiversity celebration week is a week-long event that aims to change that by celebrating and embracing the spectrum of the human mind, emotions, and personality.

Who does it impact?

People from all over the world who relate to Neurodiversity, especially people who identify as Neurodivergent.

Why is it important?

Neurodiversity provides a place for people with disabilities to learn acceptance, empowerment and self-worth. It also gives a platform for families and communities to become more aware of diversity within our society.

Important hashtags: #Neurodiversity #Diversity #BrainSciences

LET'S UNLOCK

How can I add value to this community?

What activities could I plan to support this awareness day?

How can I show my support on social Media?

How can I continue the momentum?

March 16: Marks Publication of the First Black Newspaper in America

What is it about?

The freedom's journal was the first African-American Newspaper to be published in America. The first issue was published on March 16, 1827. It was founded by Rev. John Wilk and other free black men in New York.

Who does it impact?

People of colour.

Why is it important?

This day marks the first time that a publication by an African American was made public and widely available, which played a huge part in history and contributed to progress.

Important hashtags: #FirstBlackNewspaper

LET'S UNLOCK

How can I add value to this community?

What activities could I plan to support this awareness day?

How can I show my support on social Media?

How can I continue the momentum?

March 17: St. Patrick's Day (Irish/U.S.)

What is it about?

Saint Patrick's Day, or the Feast of Saint Patrick, is a cultural and religious celebration held on 17 March, the traditional death date of the most commonly-named patron saint of Ireland, Saint Patrick.

Who does it impact?

Irish people and Christians

Why is it important?

Saint Patrick's Day was made an official feast day in the early seventeenth century and has gradually become a secular celebration of Irish culture in general. The influence of this holiday and its traditions are still prevalent today and reflect on the movements that were made to spread this cultural heritage.

Important hashtags: #stpatricksday #saintpatrick #saintpatricksday

LET'S UNLOCK

How can I add value to this community?

What activities could I plan to support this awareness day?

How can I show my support on social Media?

How can I continue the momentum?

March 24: Holi

What is it about?

Holi is a Hindu festival also known as the festival of colours observed in India and Nepal.

It's a time when people get together with family and friends to cleanse themselves of their problems, and celebrate the victory of good over evil.

Who does it impact?

People from all over the world who observe Holi, especially adherents to Hinduism.

Why is it important?

Holi is a celebration of new beginnings, in which we can start fresh and can be grateful for what we have in our lives. It's a colourful celebration where lots of people have fun throwing coloured paint at each other. It's a time to rejoice and celebrate the relationship with our friends, family and nature.

Important hashtags: #Holi

LET'S UNLOCK

How can I add value to this community?

What activities could I plan to support this awareness day?

How can I show my support on social Media?

How can I continue the momentum?

March 21: International Day for the Elimination of Racial Discrimination

What is it about?

On March 21,1960, a group of people made a peaceful demonstration in Sharpeville against the apartheid pass laws in South Africa. Police opened fire on them, murdering 69 and injuring 180. day to remember the victims of the massacre in Sharpeville, South Africa.

This day was proclaimed by the General Assembly in 1966 and the international community was called upon to redouble its efforts to eliminate all forms of racial discrimination.

Who does it impact?

People of colour and others from diverse races

Why is it important?

It's important to remember the challenges people of color have faced due to racial discrimination and sacrifices people have made to end it. Also, the recognition and celebration of races from around the world is important to foster unity and break barriers. It is a way to recognize the accomplishments and progress made by different races despite adversity.

Important hashtags:
#InternationalDayForTheEliminationOfRacialDiscrimination
#BlackLivesMatter

LET'S UNLOCK

How can I add value to this community?

What activities could I plan to support this awareness day?

How can I show my support on social Media?

How can I continue the momentum?

March 25: National Cerebral Palsy Awareness Day

What is it about?

A day to raise awareness of people living with cerebral palsy and how to improve their quality of life.

Who does it impact?

People living with cerebral palsy along with their friends and families.

Why is it important?

To improve the lives of individuals with cerebral palsy.

Important hashtags: #CerebralPalsyAwareness #SpecialNeeds

LET'S UNLOCK

How can I add value to this community?

What activities could I plan to support this awareness day?

How can I show my support on social Media?

How can I continue the momentum?

March 10: Ramadan (Islamic)

What is it about?

Ramadan Kareem to our Muslim brothers and sisters. Ramadan is the holy month of fasting, prayer and reflection. It was observed by Muhammad, the prophet of Islam, who said that Allah's beloved angels came to earth every year during Ramadan to search for those in tune with God.

Who does it impact?

Muslims very much, but also people who follow other religions that celebrate holidays similar to this one.

Why is it important?

Ramadan is a holy month of worship and ritual, and is observed by Muslims around the world. It is one of the most important occasions for Muslims to be aware of God's will and explore themselves for their purpose in life.

Important hashtags: #RamadanKareem #RamadanMubarak #Ramadan

LET'S UNLOCK

How can I add value to this community?

What activities could I plan to support this awareness day?

How can I show my support on social Media?

How can I continue the momentum?

March 30: World Bipolar Day

What is it about?

Bipolar is a mental illness that affects over 1m people in the UK and over 6 million Americans

On March 30, the world comes together to raise awareness about Bipolar.

Who does it impact?

People affected by Bipolar and their loved ones.

Why is it important?

Bipolar affects millions of people around the world. It's important to raise awareness about it and provide support for people affected.

Important Hashtags #Bipolar #WorldBipolarday

LET'S UNLOCK

How can I add value to this community?

What activities could I plan to support this awareness day?

How can I show my support on social Media?

How can I continue the momentum?

March 21: World Down Syndrome Day

What is it about?

Down syndrome is a naturally occurring chromosomal disorder in arrangement that causes intellectual and developmental delay. This day was created to educate the community about Down Syndrome and it's effects. It was first observed in 2004 and it focuses on the inclusion of people living with Down Syndrome into the society and creating opportunities for them.

Who does it impact?

People from around the world who are concerned about issues relating to genetics.

Why is it important?

It's important because Down Syndrome is a genetic disorder that affects 1 in every 691 babies. It occurs due to an error during meiosis, which causes an extra copy of chromosome 21 to be present in cells. Down Syndrome is associated with physical abnormalities and intellectual disability, but people afflicted by Down Syndrome can lead normal lives. It's important to remember that people with Down Syndrome are just like everyone else, and should be treated accordingly.

Important hashtags: #DownSyndromeDay #DSActionDay

LET'S UNLOCK

How can I add value to this community?

What activities could I plan to support this awareness day?

How can I show my support on social Media?

How can I continue the momentum?

March

March 24: Palm Sunday

What is it about?

Palm Sunday is a celebration of triumphant entry of Jesus Christ into Jerusalem on a colt.

Most of the crowd spread their garments while some cut tree branches and laid them to welcome him. This event is recorded in all four Canonical Gospels. The day is also called Passion Sunday.

Who does it impact?

People of the Christian faith from around the world.

Why is it important?

Palm Sunday is the day Christians remember and celebrate Jesus' triumphal entry into Jerusalem. It also reminds Christians about the sacrificial death of Jesus Christ for the sins of the world. The day is important because it marks the beginning of Holy Week, which leads up to Easter.

Important hashtags: #PalmSunday #Jesus #HolyWeek

LET'S UNLOCK

How can I add value to this community?

What activities could I plan to support this awareness day?

How can I show my support on social Media?

How can I continue the momentum?

March 28: Maundy Thursday

What is it about?

Maundy Thursday is a special time to reflect on the final days of Jesus Christ. This day reminds us about the final passover Jesus celebrated with the disciples before he was crucified and Jesus' instruction to the disciples: "Love one another as I have loved you"

It's a time to reflect and see if we have fulfilled Jesus' instruction of showing love to our neighbours as he has to us.

Who does it impact?

Christians all over the world.

Why is it important?

Maundy Thursday is important because it represents a time to reflect on the humility and sacrifice of Jesus. It is a time to renew our faith and focus on God.

Important hashtags: #MaundyThursday #Christianity

LET'S UNLOCK

How can I add value to this community?

```



```

What activities could I plan to support this awareness day?

```



```

How can I show my support on social Media?

```



```

How can I continue the momentum?

```



```

March 29: Good Friday (Christianity)

What is it about?

"Greater love has no one than this: to lay down one's life for one's friends." John 15:13

Good Friday symbolizes the ultimate price Jesus paid to rescue us from the consequences of our sins.

It's not as hard to lay down your life for your family or even friends compared to someone who wronged you. Yet, that is the ultimate price Jesus paid for you and me to be saved when he was crucified on the cross.

Good Friday is dedicated to remembering this sacrifice.

Who does it impact?

Christians.

Why is it important?

Good Friday is a time for you to remember that Jesus paid the ultimate price for your sins. It's a time to move closer to God and devote yourself to righteousness.

Important hashtag: #GoodFriday

LET'S UNLOCK

How can I add value to this community?

What activities could I plan to support this awareness day?

How can I show my support on social Media?

How can I continue the momentum?

March 31: Easter (Christianity)

What is it about?

He is Risen!

After 3 days in the tomb, Jesus overcame the power of death and arose from the grave to prove that he is truly God just as he prophesied.

The Messiah is Risen and we are no longer slaves to sin. Hallelujah!

Who does it impact?

Christians all over the world.

Why is it important?

Easter represents a time to reflect on the life of Jesus and recommit ourselves to God

Important hashtags: #Easter #Christianity

LET'S UNLOCK

How can I add value to this community?

What activities could I plan to support this awareness day?

How can I show my support on social Media?

How can I continue the momentum?

April 2024

Sunday	Monday	Tuesday	Wednesday	Thursday	Friday	Saturday
31	1	2 World Autism Awareness Day (U.K.)	3	4	5	6
7 World Health Day	8	9	10	11	12	13 **Songkran (Thai New Year) (Buddhist)
14	15 Jackie Robinson Day	16	17 Emancipation Day (U.S.)	18	19	20 **First Day of Ridvan (Baha'i)
21	22 Earth Day (International) **Lesbian Visibility Week Passover (Jewish)	23	24 **Theravada New Year (Buddhist)	25	26	27
28 **World Day for Safety & Health at Work **Ninth Day of Ridvan (Baha'i	29	30	1	2	3	4

**Awareness Day or Month not included in the overview

((Autism Awareness Month   **Lesbian Visibility Week

((Stress Awareness Month   April 25-27: Gathering of Nations (U.S)

((Celebrate Diversity Month

April 2: World Autism Awareness Day (U.K.)

What is it about?

Autism spectrum disorder is a neurodevelopmental disability. People with autism have communication, behavioural and intelligence impairment which manifests as having difficulties interacting with other people, taking longer to understand things or repeating the same thing several times.

The effect on communication, behaviour and intelligence are highly variable from person to person.

April 2 is a day to recognize the achievements of people with autism as well as their challenges and efforts being made to improve their quality of life.

Who does it impact?

People with autism and those who care about them.

Why is it important?

It is an important day for the recognition of people with autism and those who live with them because many people with autism face stigmatization and are unable to communicate, which can be frustrating and can make their day difficult. Because of this, we celebrate their achievements and push for better treatment for them.

Important hashtags: #WorldAutismAwarenessDay

LET'S UNLOCK

How can I add value to this community?

What activities could I plan to support this awareness day?

How can I show my support on social Media?

How can I continue the momentum?

April 22: Passover (Jewish)

What is it about?

"And the blood shall be to you for a token upon the houses where ye are: and when I see the blood, I will pass over you, and there shall no plague be upon you to destroy you, when I smite the land of Egypt" Exodus 12:13.

The exodus is one of the most iconic stories in the Torah. The Passover signifies how God spared the lives of the Israelites when the Egyptians were smote for not liberating the Israelites from slavery.

Eventually, pharaoh let the Israelites go but not without a fight. The Egyptian army chased the Israelites on their way out but were drowned in the red sea after the Israelites passed.

Who celebrates it?

Jewish people.

Why is it important?

It is an important part of Jewish tradition. It is a time for reflection and gratefulness to God for the supernatural Exodus of the Israelites from Egypt.

Important hashtags: #Passover #Seder #SederDay

LET'S UNLOCK

How can I add value to this community?

What activities could I plan to support this awareness day?

How can I show my support on social Media?

How can I continue the momentum?

April 7: World Health Day

What is it about?

Health is life. Health is the reason why you can work, play, learn, think and do all the things you want.

World Health Day is a day to re-emphasize the importance of health and encourage practices that promote good and sound health.

Who does it impact?

Everyone

Why is it important?

It's important to raise awareness about our health as it is vital to our well being.

Important Hashtags #Health #WorldHealthDay

LET'S UNLOCK

How can I add value to this community?

What activities could I plan to support this awareness day?

How can I show my support on social Media?

How can I continue the momentum?

April 15: Jackie Robinson Day

What is it about:

Until 1947, players of black African descent were excluded from major league baseball.
Jackie Robinson was the first black man to play for a major league baseball team and break the racial barrier on the baseball field.

He was also a leader in the civil rights struggle for African Americans.

Who does it impact?

People of colour.

Why is it important?

Jackie Robinson paved the way for other African Americans into Major league teams and had huge contributions to making a difference in America's history.

Important hashtags: #JackieRobinsonDay #JackieRobinson

LET'S UNLOCK

How can I add value to this community?

What activities could I plan to support this awareness day?

How can I show my support on social Media?

How can I continue the momentum?

April 17: Emancipation Day (U.S.)

What is it about?

Emancipation day is the celebration of the freedom of African Americans from the shackles of slavery. It reminds us of the horrors of slavery and why we must always condemn it.

Who does it impact?

People of colour.

Why is it important?

The emancipation of slaves from America plays a huge part in history, as well as the fact that many people at the time did not agree with this action. Therefore, by celebrating and commemorating those who were emancipated, we recognize their progress.

Important hashtags: #EmancipationDay #BlackLivesMatter #AbolitionOfSlavery

LET'S UNLOCK

How can I add value to this community?

What activities could I plan to support this awareness day?

How can I show my support on social Media?

How can I continue the momentum?

April 22: Earth Day (International)

What is it about?

No matter your gender, sexual orientation, religion or race, Mother earth is home to us all and we have to take care of it.

We all have a part to play because our actions or inactions have consequences.

Earth day is dedicated to reminding us about our environment and the role we must play to keep the earth habitable for us all.

Who does it impact?

This one impacts everyone because we all live on earth and therefore we have a role to play to protect Mother earth.

Why is it important?

It's important that we take care of our planet, it's all we got. At least, until we find another habitable planet.

Important hashtags: #EarthDay #SaveThePlanet #GoGreen #Recycle #Sustainability #ClimateAction #ClimateChange #SaveOurPlanet #ActOnClimate #DoYourPart

LET'S UNLOCK

How can I add value to this community?

What activities could I plan to support this awareness day?

How can I show my support on social Media?

How can I continue the momentum?

April 25-27: Gathering of Nations (U.S)

What is it about?

The Gathering of Nations is an annual event that brings together a rainbow of cultures from around the world. It always takes place on Native American land and at the request of the Cherokee Nation. This event has been held yearly since 1995 in Tahlequah, Oklahoma to promote cultural understanding.

Who does it impact?

People who are interested in other cultures, as well as human rights activists and people concerned with social inequality.

Why is it important?

It is an important event because it fosters tolerance, understanding, and cultural communication. All people who are interested in the concerns of other races should be interested in this special event.

Important hashtags: #GatheringofNations

LET'S UNLOCK

How can I add value to this community?

What activities could I plan to support this awareness day?

How can I show my support on social Media?

How can I continue the momentum?

May 2023

Sunday	Monday	Tuesday	Wednesday	Thursday	Friday	Saturday
28	29	30	1	2	3	4
5 Cinco de Mayo (Mexican American)	6	7	8	9	10	11
12	13	14	15 Birthday of the Buddha	16 ** Global Accessibility Awarness Day	17 International Day Against Homophobia, Transphobia, and Biphobia (LGBTQ+) Malcolm X Day	18
19 Pentecost	20	21 **World Day for Cultural Diversity for Dialogue and Development	22	23 **Vesak/ Visakha Puja (Buddhist)	24	25 African Liberation Day
26	27	28	29	30	31	1

Mental Health Awareness Month

**Awareness Day or Month not included in the overview

ALS Awareness Month (U.S.)

May 6-12: Deaf Awareness Week (U.K.)

May 13-19: Black Inclusion Week (U.K.)

May

May: Mental Health Awareness Month

What is it about?

Without any doubt, our physical health is crucial to our well being. But your mental health is just as important too.

Mental health refers to your emotional, cognitive and behavioural state. Your mental health controls the state of your mind and determines how and what you think.

May is a month to share awareness about mental health, clear misconceptions and strengthen those who may be

Who does it impact?

People with mental illnesses, people who want to learn more about mental health, and those who care about them.

Why is it important?

Mental health is often overlooked but it can have a significant impact on a person's life. Therefore, we should ensure proper treatment for those with mental illness and provide proper emotional support for this population.

Important hashtags: #MentalHealthAwarenessMonth #mentalhealthawareness #mentalhealthmatters #mentalhealthrecovery

LET'S UNLOCK

How can I add value to this community?

What activities could I plan to support this awareness day?

How can I show my support on social Media?

How can I continue the momentum?

The 3rd Sunday in May is "Malcolm X Day"

What is it about?

A day to honour the legacy of one of the most influential African Americans of all time. A man who fought racism and inequality all his life, Malcolm X.

Who does it impact?

People of colour, those who want to learn more about his life and impact, and those who care about him.

Why is it important?

Malcolm X was one of the greatest leaders in American history and pushed for justice with his fight against racism and inequality. He was a man who paved the way for many other activists and continues to be an inspiration to those today.

Important hashtags: #MalcolmXDay #BlackLivesMatter

LET'S UNLOCK

How can I add value to this community?

What activities could I plan to support this awareness day?

How can I show my support on social Media?

How can I continue the momentum?

May 5: Cinco de Mayo (Mexican American)

What is it about?

Cinco de Mayo is a holiday that commemorates the Battle of Puebla, a major victory against foreign invaders. It was originally intended to remind Mexicans of the sacrifices made by their ancestors.

Who does it impact?

Mexican Americans, but also people with similar cultural backgrounds to other Latin American countries.

Why is it important?

It's important in Mexican culture because it reminds them of their heritage and provides a sense of unity for people with similar ancestry.

Important hashtags: #CincoDeMayo #CincoDeMayo2017 #LatinosUnidos

LET'S UNLOCK

How can I add value to this community?

What activities could I plan to support this awareness day?

How can I show my support on social Media?

How can I continue the momentum?

May 15: Birthday of the Buddha

What is it about?

The Birthday of the Buddha is celebrated on the day when Siddhartha Gautama was born. It is also known as Wesak or Buddha Day and has been observed since 623 BCE.

Who does it impact?

Buddhists worldwide, and those who are interested in Buddhist teachings.

Why is it important?

The Birthday of the Buddha is a time for people to reflect on the teachings of Gautama Buddha, as well as on their own thoughts and discoveries.

Important hashtags: #BuddhaDay #HappyBuddhaDay #Buddhism

LET'S UNLOCK

How can I add value to this community?

```
[                                                                    ]
```

What activities could I plan to support this awareness day?

```
[                                                                    ]
```

How can I show my support on social Media?

```
[                                                                    ]
```

How can I continue the momentum?

```
[                                                                    ]
```

May 13-19: Black Inclusion Week (U.K.)

What is it about?

Black people suffer from stereotyping and discrimination of various forms till this very moment. As a society, we all have a part to play to break these stereotypes.

Black inclusion week is a time to remind us to change the narrative about blacks and celebrate the achievements of black people in the UK across all walks of life.

Who does it impact?

People from all over the world who are concerned with Inclusion and Diversity initiatives. This includes all races, genders, ages, sexual orientations and disabilities.

Why is it important?

Black Inclusion Week is important because it's a way to celebrate the successes of the black community. This includes their contributions to society, as well as their resistance to inequality.

Important hashtags: #BlackInclusionWeek #Diversity

LET'S UNLOCK

How can I add value to this community?

What activities could I plan to support this awareness day?

How can I show my support on social Media?

How can I continue the momentum?

May 17: International Day Against Homophobia, Transphobia, and Biphobia (LGBTQ+)

What is it about?

Flying a pride flag comes at a cost in some parts of the world. Discrimination. Hate. Violence and even death in some cases. May 17 is dedicated to creating awareness against discrimination of LGBTQ+ individuals and communities.

Who does it impact?

LGBTQ+ individuals, their families, and their friends.

Why is it important?

It's important because everyone deserves to be heard and respected for who they are. It is a day to promote love, tolerance, equality, and understanding.

Important hashtags: #Equality #Pride #LGBTQ #IDAHOTB

LET'S UNLOCK

How can I add value to this community?

What activities could I plan to support this awareness day?

How can I show my support on social Media?

How can I continue the momentum?

May 25: African Liberation Day

What is it about?

A day to recognize the achievements of the people who fought against slavery and racism for liberation.

Who does it impact?

People of colour and those who want to learn more about them.

Why is it important?

The fight for freedom from slavery must always be remembered because it was an important part of history and a major step in progress. May 25 is particularly important to Africans in the Diaspora because it is the date for the official independence of many African nations which occurred after they struggled against colonialism.

Important hashtags: #AfricanLiberationDay #BlackLivesMatter #ALD

LET'S UNLOCK

How can I add value to this community?

What activities could I plan to support this awareness day?

How can I show my support on social Media?

How can I continue the momentum?

May 19: Pentecost

What is it about?

50 days after the resurrection of Jesus Christ, the Holy Spirit descended on the apostles and they began to speak in tongues.

Pentecost is the celebration of this coming of the holy spirit on the apostles.

Who does it impact?

Christians around the world

Why is it important?

Pentecost is an important holiday in the Christian calendar because it commemorates the descent of the Holy Spirit upon the Apostles and the Virgin Mary.

Important hashtags: #pentecostal, #godisgood #blessed

LET'S UNLOCK

How can I add value to this community?

What activities could I plan to support this awareness day?

How can I show my support on social Media?

How can I continue the momentum?

June 2023

Monday	Tuesday	Wednesday	Thursday	Friday	Saturday	Sunday
27	28	29	30	31	1	2
3 **Growing for Wellbeing Week (3rd – 9th June)	4	5 **World Environment Day	6	7	8 **Global Wellness Day	9 **Race Unity Day (U.S.) "Odunde Festival," or African New Year
10	11 Shavuot	12 Loving Day Odunde Festival	13	14 **Hajj (Islam)	15	16 **Martyrdom of Guru Arjan Dev (Sikh) **Fathers Day Eid al-Adha (Islam)
17	18 **Autistic Pride Day	19 Juneteenth, (AKA "Freedom Day" or "Emancipation Day")	20 Summer Solstice **World Refugee Day	21	22 Windrush Day (U.K.)	23
24	25	26	27	28	29	30

LGBT Pride Month

Caribbean American Heritage Month (U.S.)

African American Music Appreciation Month

June 10-16: Men's Health Week

**Gypsy, Roma and Traveller Month

**Awareness Day or Month not included in the overview

June

June: LGBT Pride Month

What is it about?

Pride month is a time to commemorate the stonewall protest on June 28, 1969. This protest would be a turning point in the activism for equal rights for the LGBT+ community.

Pride month is a time to remember the challenges and achievements of the LGBT+ community in overcoming discrimination, getting equal rights and acceptance into society.

Who does it impact?

LGBTQ+ individuals, their families and friends.

Why is it important?

It's important because everyone deserves to be heard and respected for who they are. It is a time to promote love, tolerance, equality and understanding.

Important hashtags: #PrideMonth #LGBTQ #LGBTQPride #GayPride

LET'S UNLOCK

How can I add value to this community?

What activities could I plan to support this awareness day?

How can I show my support on social Media?

How can I continue the momentum?

June: Caribbean American Heritage Month (U.S.)

What is it about?

Caribbean American Heritage Month is observed during June in the United States. It was signed into law in 2006 by President George W. Bush to celebrate the contributions of Caribbean Americans. The intention was to recognize the Hispanic cultures, heritage, experiences and to encourage cultural understanding.

Who does it impact?

Caribbean Americans, and those who want to be more informed on their experiences in the U.S.

Why is it important?

It is important because Caribbean Americans are a diverse, vibrant, and strong community. The government needs to recognise their contributions to American society.

Important hashtags: #CaribbeanAmericanHeritageMonth #CaribbeanAmericanHeritage

LET'S UNLOCK

How can I add value to this community?

```



```

What activities could I plan to support this awareness day?

```



```

How can I show my support on social Media?

```



```

How can I continue the momentum?

```



```

June: African American Music Appreciation Month

What is it about?

In the past decades, the Music Industry has produced lots of successful African American artists that have made an impact on a global scale. The likes of Whitney Houston, Michael Jackson, Jay Z, Beyonce, Prince, Jimi Hendrix, Ray Charles, Kanye West etc. This month is dedicated to recognizing the contributions of African American to the music industry over the years.

Who does it impact?

People who love music, especially music from African Americans.

Why is it important?

Music from African American people has been a major influence on music as a whole and their influence is something we should always be aware of and appreciate.

Important hashtags: #AfricanAmericanMusicAppreciationMonth #AAMAM #blackouttuesday

LET'S UNLOCK

How can I add value to this community?

What activities could I plan to support this awareness day?

How can I show my support on social Media?

How can I continue the momentum?

June 11: Shavuot

What is it about?

Shavuot is a Jewish holiday that is celebrated around the world on the 49th day of the Hebrew month of Nisan. It marks the giving of the Torah to Moses and celebrates one of the most important events in Jewish history.

Who does it impact?

Jews who celebrate Shavuot, especially those who follow Orthodox Judaism.

Why is it important?

Shavuot highlights the importance of religious beliefs and the importance of following traditions. It can also be a time for reflection and growth.

Important hashtags: #Shavuot #WorldShavuot

LET'S UNLOCK

How can I add value to this community?

What activities could I plan to support this awareness day?

How can I show my support on social Media?

How can I continue the momentum?

June 12: Loving Day

What is it about?

Imagine you could not marry the love of your life because you were of different races.

Until 1967, this was the reality in America. Interracial marriages were not allowed until the landmark civil rights decision by the Supreme Court that a ban on interracial marriage was a violation of Equal Protection and Due Process clauses of the 14th amendment.

Who does it impact?

People who are in interracial marriages or relationships.

Why is it important?

Although Loving Day was started to acknowledge inter-racial relationships, it is a day for people of all races in love to celebrate their relationships with one another. It is a day to remind ourselves of the power love has and the culture of "love over hate" that we should strive for.

Important hashtags: #LoveWins #LovingDay #InterracialFamilyDay

LET'S UNLOCK

How can I add value to this community?

```



```

What activities could I plan to support this awareness day?

```



```

How can I show my support on social Media?

```



```

How can I continue the momentum?

```



```

June 12: "Odunde Festival," or African New Year

What is it about?

It is an annual African-American street festival held in the African-American cultural district of Philadelphia, Pennsylvania, on and around South Street. It is the largest and oldest African-American street festival in the United States and is one of the largest and most popular street festivals in Philadelphia.

Who does it impact?

People of African descent and those who care about them.

Why is it important?

Odunde is an important festival that recognizes the richness and diversity of African heritage, culture, and community. It provides a day for people to celebrate the beauty that Africans have added to this world, and it is a way for us to remember the struggles and triumphs of our ancestors.

Important hashtags: #OdundeFestival #AfricanAmericanHeritageMonth

LET'S UNLOCK

How can I add value to this community?

What activities could I plan to support this awareness day?

How can I show my support on social Media?

How can I continue the momentum?

June 10-16: Men's Health Week

What is it about?

Men's Health Week is a week to educate the public about how men can improve the state of their health.

This week gives an opportunity to encourage men and boys to seek regular medical advice and early treatment for disease and injury.

Who does it impact?

Men

Why is it important?

To encourage men and boys to seek regular medical advice and early treatment for disease and injury
Important hashtags

#Menshealth

LET'S UNLOCK

How can I add value to this community?

[ ]

What activities could I plan to support this awareness day?

[ ]

How can I show my support on social Media?

[ ]

How can I continue the momentum?

[ ]

June 22: Windrush Day (U.K.)

What is it about?

On June 22 1948, 492 Caribbean immigrants moved into the UK with the Empire Windrush ship after the world war. This day is also known as "the day that changed Britain". Windrush day is a commemoration of the contribution of immigrants to the UK.

Who does it impact?

People from all over who are descendants of the Windrush immigrants. These immigrants came from Caribbean islands such as Jamaica, Barbados and Trinidad, and had been living in England illegally. They were discriminated against by both their own country and England because their arrival was so sudden after World War II.

Why is it important?

Windrush day is important because it encourages inclusion, especially in the public sector, and it celebrates their history as a part of Britain.

Important tips: #WindrushDay #windrush

LET'S UNLOCK

How can I add value to this community?

What activities could I plan to support this awareness day?

How can I show my support on social Media?

How can I continue the momentum?

June 16: Eid Al-Adha

What is it about?

Eid Al-Adha is another important Muslim holiday, which follows the holy month of Ramadan. It's considered to be a time of forgiveness and sacrifice, which happens on the 10th day after a full moon. The corresponding date for the next one is tentatively beginning on the evening of June 16, 2024 and ends June 19, 2024.

Who does it impact?

Muslims from all over the world who observe Eid al-Adha

Why is it important?

Eid Al-Adha is important because it encourages understanding of the importance of forgiveness and sacrifice in the context of religion and how those values can impact our daily lives.

Impoartant hashtags: #EidAlAdha #EidMubarak

LET'S UNLOCK

How can I add value to this community?

What activities could I plan to support this awareness day?

How can I show my support on social Media?

How can I continue the momentum?

June 19: Juneteenth, (AKA "Freedom Day" or "Emancipation Day")

What is it about?

The history of America is dented with slavery but in fact, that is where the Juneteenth celebration stems from. The Juneteenth celebration is a Commomeration of the emancipation of slaves.

It serves as a reminder of the mistakes made in the past so we do not repeat the same mistake.

Who does it impact?

People of African descent and those who care about them.

Why is it important?

The ending of slavery was an important moment in history that we should always celebrate. It was a major step forward in the fight against racism, and it gave our ancestors the freedom to pursue a better life for themselves.

Important hashtags: #FreedomDay #BlackLivesMatter #EmancipationDay #Juneteenth

LET'S UNLOCK

How can I add value to this community?

What activities could I plan to support this awareness day?

How can I show my support on social Media?

How can I continue the momentum?

July 2024

Sunday	Monday	Tuesday	Wednesday	Thursday	Friday	Saturday
25	1	2	3	4 ** Independence Day (U.S.)	5 **Birthday of Guru Hargobind (Sikh)	6 Al-Hijri (Islamic)
7	8	9	10	11	12	13
14 International Non-Binary People's Day	15	16 **Ashura (Islam)	17	18 Black Leadership Day	19 The Maafa Commemoration	20
21 **Asalha Puja (Dharma Day) (Buddhist)	22	23 Birthday of Emperor Haile Selassie (Rastafari)	24 Nelson Mandela International Day	25 National Schizophrenia Awareness Day	26	27
28 **World Hepatitis Day	29	30 **International Day of Friendship **World Day against Trafficking Persons	31	1	2	3
4	5	6	7	8	9	10

Disability Pride Month

July 18th - 17th August South Asian Heritage Month

**Awareness days or month not included in overview

July

July: Disability Pride Month

What is it about?

Disability Pride Month is observed every year by people with physical, mental and intellectual disabilities, their friends and families. It's a month for people with disabilities to celebrate their talents and show that behind their disability they have abilities.

Who does it impact?

People from all over the world who are associated with disability, especially those who are aware of or directly related to people with disabilities.

Why is it important?

Disability Pride Month is important because it reminds people that all disabled people are individuals first and are worthy of respect. It also reminds them of the importance of acceptance and inclusion for all people, no matter what type of disability they have.

Important hashtags: #DisabilityPrideMonth #disability

LET'S UNLOCK

How can I add value to this community?

What activities could I plan to support this awareness day?

How can I show my support on social Media?

How can I continue the momentum?

July 18th - 17th August South Asian Heritage Month

What is it about?

It's always important to take pride in your heritage. Your heritage is your strength. It is who you are at the core of your being.

The month of August is dedicated to celebrating people with roots in the South Asian countries of India, Pakistan, Afghanistan, Bangladesh, Sri Lanka, Nepal, Bhutan, and the Maldives.

Who does it impact?

People from all over the world who identify as South Asian

Why is it important?

Recognizing and celebrating our heritage keeps it alive.

Important hashtags: #southasianawarenessmonth

LET'S UNLOCK

How can I add value to this community?

What activities could I plan to support this awareness day?

How can I show my support on social Media?

How can I continue the momentum?

July 14: International Non-Binary People's Day

What is it about?

Non-binary refers to a person who doesn't identify as a man or woman. Life for non-binary people is multi layered and can seem complex but the best way to understand them is to listen.

International Non-Binary People's Day was established to honour and create awareness about non-binary people all over the world.

Who does it impact?

People from all over the world who identify as non-binary.

Why is it important?

Non-binary people are important to celebrate because they are a part of the human race and deserve recognition for their identity.

Important hashtags: #InternationalNonBinaryPeopleDay #nonbinary #genderqueer #genderfluid

LET'S UNLOCK

How can I add value to this community?

What activities could I plan to support this awareness day?

How can I show my support on social Media?

How can I continue the momentum?

July 18: Nelson Mandela International Day

What Is It about?

Nelson Mandela was no ordinary man. He was an activist who spoke against the all white government in South Africa for their apartheid laws that saw blacks in South Africa suffer racial segregation.

Even in the face of death, he kept going. He has a famous speech at his trial where he said he was ready to die. He was sent to prison and spent 27 years there. Even while he was in prison, he never gave up or caved in to pressure to give up the fight. He was steadfast until he was eventually released and then became the first black South African president. Resilience.

Who does it impact?

People of African descent who want to learn more about him, and those who care about him.

Why is it important?

Nelson Mandela was a man who fought for justice and equality during his life, and continues to be an inspiration for change in Africa today. He is a man who should be celebrated for his impact and influence on the world.

Important hashtags: #NelsonMandelaDay #MandelaDay, #Mandela, #NationalMandelaDay

LET'S UNLOCK

How can I add value to this community?

What activities could I plan to support this awareness day?

How can I show my support on social Media?

How can I continue the momentum?

July 18: Black Leadership Day

What is it about?

Black Leaders Awareness Day (BLAD) spotlights historic and current black leaders who have made significant impact in the world.

The event also serves as a showcase for black-owned businesses and promotes diversity in public office.

Who does it impact?

Black people who are interested in social issues, but also those who are interested in inclusion and equality for everyone.

Why is it important?

It's important to celebrate the struggles and accomplishments of black people so that people everywhere can learn from their experiences.

Important hashtags: #BlackJuly18 #BlackExcellence #BlackPowerJobs

LET'S UNLOCK

How can I add value to this community?

```
```

What activities could I plan to support this awareness day?

```
```

How can I show my support on social Media?

```
```

How can I continue the momentum?

```
```

July 19: The Maafa Commemoration

What is it about?

A day to honour slaves who went through unimaginable atrocities, horror and anguish. Through performance art, ritual and prayer, our souls are healed od the pain and the chains of the legacy of slavery is broken.

Who does it impact?

People of African descent and those who want to learn more about the history of slavery.

Why is it important?

The Maafa is a very dark part of our history, but we cannot forget it because if we do so then we are doomed to repeat its mistakes. We must always remember the atrocities that were committed because they are a reminder of how far we have come and how far we still need to go.

Important hashtags: #MaafaMemorialDay #BlackLivesMatter #Maafacommemoration #blm #Racialjustice #equality #Humanrights

LET'S UNLOCK

How can I add value to this community?

What activities could I plan to support this awareness day?

How can I show my support on social Media?

How can I continue the momentum?

July 25: National Schizophrenia Awareness Day

What is it about?

Schizophrenia is a complex condition that affects how a person thinks, feels and experiences the world around them.

25 July is a day to talk about the challenges faced by people living with schizophrenia in the UK and millions more worldwide. It also looks at how we can tackle some of the stigma and discrimination surrounding this illness.

Who does it impact?

People living with Schizophrenia and their loved ones.

Why is it important?

To shed light on the challenges of Schizophrenia and how we can provide support.

Important hashtags #NationalSchizophreniaawarenessday

LET'S UNLOCK

How can I add value to this community?

```

```

What activities could I plan to support this awareness day?

```

```

How can I show my support on social Media?

```

```

How can I continue the momentum?

```

```

July 6: Al-Hijri (Islamic)

What is it about?

Al-Hijri is the Islamic New Year. It occurs on the first day of the Islamic month of Muharram and marks the beginning of a new year in Muslim countries around the world. The date changes every year due to differences in the lunar calendar. The next one is tentatively beginning on the evening of July 6, 2024 and ends July 7, 2024.

Who does it impact?

Muslims around the world.

Why is it important?

The festival is a time to commemorate the end of a good year and start a new one. The celebration is a way to honour the faith and people who have passed away. Muslims also look for guidance for the coming year through surahs of the Quran.

Important hashtags: #NewYear #Islam #Muharram #FestivalOfMosques

LET'S UNLOCK

How can I add value to this community?

What activities could I plan to support this awareness day?

How can I show my support on social Media?

How can I continue the momentum?

July 23: The birthday of Haile Selassie (Rastafari)

What is it about?

Emperor Haile Selassie I was known for modernizing his country, for helping to establish the Organization of African Unity in 1963 and for being overthrown in 1974. He was regarded as the messiah of the African race by many Rasta.

July 23 is a day to celebrate the life of the Emperor of Ethiopia who inspired the Rastafari movement.

Who does it impact?

People of African descent who practice Rastafari, and others who respect him.

Why is it important?

Haile Selassie was an extremely influential figure in world history who not only inspired a huge following but also gave Africans a source of pride during a time when they were being oppressed and marginalized. He was a man who was loved by many, and he should always be remembered for his contributions to humanity.

Important hashtags: #HaileSelassieBirthday #Rastafari #HaileSelassie #Ethiopia

LET'S UNLOCK

How can I add value to this community?

```



```

What activities could I plan to support this awareness day?

```



```

How can I show my support on social Media?

```



```

How can I continue the momentum?

```



```

August 2024

Sunday	Monday	Tuesday	Wednesday	Thursday	Friday	Saturday
30	31	1	2	1	2	3
4	5	6	7	8	9 International Day of the World's Indigenous People (U.N.)	10
11	12 International Youth Day	13 Marking the adoption of the Pan-African flag	14	15 Feast of the Assumption (Roman Catholic)	16	17 UK Black Pride Power Marcus Garvey Day
18	19 **World Humanitarian Day **Raksha Bandhan (Hindu)	20	21 **Internationational Day for the Remembrance of the Slave Tade and its Abolition ** Senior Citizen's Day (U.S.)	22 International Day Commemorating the Victims of Acts of Violence based on Religion or Belief	23	24 **Feast of Saint Bartholomew the Apostle (Christian)
24	26 Krishna Janmashtami Women's Equality Day	27	28	29	30 **Grief Awarness Day	31

August 1-7: World Breastfeeding week

** National Civility Month

**Awareness Day or Month not included in the overview

August

August 1-7: World Breastfeeding week

What is it about?

Breastfeeding is one of the best ways to ensure child growth and development. In fact, the World Health Organization advises 6 months of exclusive breastfeeding.

The first week of August(1-7) is World Breastfeeding Week and is meant to create awareness on the importance of breastfeeding and how to create a society that is more enabling for nursing mothers.

Who does it impact?

Lactating mothers and their families.

Why is it important?

It's vital to create awareness about the importance of breastfeeding.

Important hashtags #Worldbreastfeedingday

LET'S UNLOCK

How can I add value to this community?

```



```

What activities could I plan to support this awareness day?

```



```

How can I show my support on social Media?

```



```

How can I continue the momentum?

```



```

August 9: International Day of the World's Indigenous People (U.N.)

What is it about?

Did you know there are over 370 million indigenous people in more than 90 countries. Sadly, many indigenous people have been forced out of their regions due to industrialization, conflict and other factors. Sometimes this makes them lose their cultural identity.

The International Day of the World's Indigenous People is an official United Nations holiday that is held on August 9 to celebrate the diverse cultures around the world, encourage the protection of their lives and territories.

Who does it impact?

Indigenous people from all over the world, their families and friends.

Why is it important?

It's important because it is a day to acknowledge all of the cultures that make up the world. It's important to understand the diversity of human culture.

Important hashtags: #WorldIndigenousDay #IndigenousPeople #UN

LET'S UNLOCK

How can I add value to this community?

What activities could I plan to support this awareness day?

How can I show my support on social Media?

How can I continue the momentum?

August 12: International Youth Day

What is it about?

The youth of today are the leaders of tomorrow. International youths day advocates for the right of young people to education, healthcare, employment etc. It celebrates the contributions of youths to making society a better place for all.

Who does it Impact?

Youths all around the world.

Why is it important?

It's important to advocate for the rights of the youths, create awareness for their challenges and provide solutions to help youths live a quality life. Important hashtags:

#InternationalYouthDay #Youth

LET'S UNLOCK

How can I add value to this community?

What activities could I plan to support this awareness day?

How can I show my support on social Media?

How can I continue the momentum?

August 13: Marking the adoption of the Pan-African flag

What is it about?

A day to celebrate the Pan-African flag and honour the people who created it. The red, black and green colours of the flag were adopted in 1920 in recognition of people of colour.

Who does it impact?

People of African descent, particularly those in the Diaspora, who want to learn more about the flag.

Why is it important?

The Pan-African flag is another symbol of African pride and unity and should be recognized for its historical value. It is a reminder of our connection as Africans around the world and a symbol of pride in our heritage.

Important hashtags: #PanAfricanFlagDay #AfricanUnity

LET'S UNLOCK

How can I add value to this community?

What activities could I plan to support this awareness day?

How can I show my support on social Media?

How can I continue the momentum?

August 17: UK Black Pride Power

What is it about?

UK Black Pride is a celebration of lesbian, gay, bisexual, transgender and queen people of colour. Started in 2005, it is now the largest celebration of LGBTQ+ people of colour in Europe.

Who does it impact?

People of colour who are part of the LGBTQ+ community.

Why is it important?

It is a celebration of the acceptance and equality of LGBTQ+ people of colour. It also raises awareness against homophobia.

Important Hashtags:
#blackpride #blackexcellence #blackpower

LET'S UNLOCK

How can I add value to this community?

What activities could I plan to support this awareness day?

How can I show my support on social Media?

How can I continue the momentum?

August 15: Feast of the Assumption (Roman Catholic)

What is it about?

The Feast of the Assumption of the Blessed Virgin Mary is one of the most important celebrations in the Catholic faith. It celebrates the Virgin Mary's ascent into Heaven or assumption. The holiday was established by Pope Pius XII in 1950 and has been widely celebrated since.

Who does it impact?

Catholics celebrate this holiday worldwide.

Why is it important?

The Feast of the Assumption is a reminder of the strength and faith of the Virgin Mary, as well as her role in the Catholic faith. It is also a time for people to express gratitude for their mothers, or other female relatives and friends that have had an impact on their lives.

Important hashtags: #HappyFeastOfTheAssumption

LET'S UNLOCK

How can I add value to this community?

What activities could I plan to support this awareness day?

How can I show my support on social Media?

How can I continue the momentum?

August 17: Marcus Garvey Day

What is it about?

Marcus Garvey was a Jamaican activist, orator and pan-Africanist leader who founded the United Negro Improvement Association and organized the first mass African exodus since slavery.

Who does it impact?

People of African descent and those who care about them.

Why is it important?

Marcus Garvey was a man who was dedicated to helping African people rise from oppression and live a better life, and his contributions should be remembered. It is important to know where we come from so that we can know where we are going.

Important hashtags: #MarcusGarveyDay #GarveyDay #MarcusGarvey

LET'S UNLOCK

How can I add value to this community?

What activities could I plan to support this awareness day?

How can I show my support on social Media?

How can I continue the momentum?

August 26: Krishna Janmashtami

What is it about?

Krishna Janmashtami, also known simply as Janmashtami, is an annual Hindu festival that celebrates the birth of Krishna, the eighth avatar of Vishnu. It is observed according to the Hindu lunisolar calendar, on the eighth day of the dark half of the month of Bhadrapada, the day after the full moon.

Who does it impact?

Hindus all over the world and those who follow the Hindu religion. Why is it important?

Krishna Janmashtami is important because it marks the birth of Krishna, one of the most important figures in Hinduism. Krishna is considered to be an Avatar of Vishnu, and his birth is celebrated as a major festival in Hinduism.

Important hashtags: #KrishnaJanmashtam, #HappyJanmashtami #HappyKrishnaJanmashtami

LET'S UNLOCK

How can I add value to this community?

What activities could I plan to support this awareness day?

How can I show my support on · ocial Media?

How can I continue the momentum?

August 26: Women's Equality Day

What is it about?

It's been just over a century since women began to vote and the struggle for women's equality has come a long way. Women's Equality Day is a United States holiday that commemorates the passage of the 19th Amendment to the Constitution which gave women the right to vote in 1920. Although the struggle for women's equality is far from over, a lot of progress has been made. It was established in 1971, by Congress and President Richard Nixon.

Who does it impact?

Women and those who want to celebrate their accomplishments.

Why is it important?

It's important because women deserve equal rights and opportunities as men. It is part of a series of holidays dedicated to honouring women for their achievements.
Important hashtags: #WomensEqualityDay

LET'S UNLOCK

How can I add value to this community?

What activities could I plan to support this awareness day?

How can I show my support on social Media?

How can I continue the momentum?

September 2024

Sunday	Monday	Tuesday	Wednesday	Thursday	Friday	Saturday
1	2 **Labor Day (U.S.)	3	4	5 **International Day of Charity	6 **Colour Blind Awareness Day **Ganesh Chaturthi (Hindu)	7
8	9	10 World Suicide Prevention Day (U.K.)	11 The Enkutatash/the Ethiopian New Year	12	13	14
15 National Hispanic Heritage Month **International Week of the Deaf **Mawlid al-Nabi(Islam)	16 **Mexican Independence Day ** Anant Chaturdashi (Hindu) Mawlid	17	18 ** International Equal Pay Day	19	20 HeForShe (Women)	21 **International Day of Peace **World Gratitude Day **World Alzheimer's Day
22 Autumnal Equinox	23 Bi Visbility Day (U.K.) **International Day of Sign Languages	24	25	26	27	28 **International Right to Know Day **World Heart Day
29 ((Umjb Bc_dB_w	30	1	2	3	4	5

September 30 - October 6: National Inclusion Week   **Awareness Day or Month not included in the overview

** World Alzheimer Month

** Latin American Heritage Month

** National Guide Dog Month (U.S.)

September 10: World Suicide Prevention Day (U.K.)

What is it about?

Every 40 seconds someone dies by suicide. Let that sink in for a moment. What this really means is that an estimated one million people die from suicide every year and the leading cause is depressoon.

World Suicide Prevention Day is observed every year on September 10th as a way for people all over the world to recognize suicide as a public health problem and to work towards preventing it.

Who does it impact?

People from all over the world who are concerned with mental health issues, especially those who have a personal connection, such as friends and family members of people who have committed suicide.

Why is it important?

World Suicide Prevention Day is important because it raises awareness of mental health issues and the ways we can prevent them.

Important hashtags: #WorldSuicidePreventionDay #endsuicideprevention #mentalhealth

LET'S UNLOCK

How can I add value to this community?

What activities could I plan to support this awareness day?

How can I show my support on social Media?

How can I continue the momentum?

September 11 (or, during Leap Year, September 12): The Enkutatash/the Ethiopian New Year

What is it about?

Enkutatash is the name for the Ethiopian new year and it means gift of jewels in amharic. The festival celebrates Ethiopian culture including traditional dancing and food.

Who does it impact?

People of African descent with Ethiopian heritage and Rastafarians.

Why is it important?

Ethiopian new year is a festival that has been celebrated for centuries, and continues to be celebrated today. It is an opportunity for people to learn about the culture of Ethiopians in the Diaspora and connect with their roots. This is especially true for Rastafarians because they believe that Ethiopia is a spiritual home for them.

Important hashtags: #Enkutatash #EthiopianNewYear

LET'S UNLOCK

How can I add value to this community?

What activities could I plan to support this awareness day?

How can I show my support on social Media?

How can I continue the momentum?

September 15: National Hispanic Heritage Month

What is it about?

Through music, food and dance, Hispanics and Latinos have greatly influenced the culture of America. The National Hispanic Heritage Month was established in 1999 by President Bill Clinton to recognize the contributions of Hispanics and their culture.

Who does it impact?

Hispanics, their families and friends.

Why is it important?

It's important because Latinos are an important part of American society, and deserve to be recognized for their contributions.

Important hashtags: #HispanicHeritageMonth #HispanicHeritage

LET'S UNLOCK

How can I add value to this community?

What activities could I plan to support this awareness day?

How can I show my support on social Media?

How can I continue the momentum?

September 16: Mawlid

What is it about?

Mawlid is the annual observance of the birthday of the Islamic prophet Muhammad which is celebrated on the 12th day of Rabi' Al-Awwal, the third month in the Islamic calendar.

Who does it impact?

Muslims all over the world

Why is it important?

The mawlid is a time for Muslims to come together and reaffirm their commitment to the Prophet Muhammad and his teachings. Finally, the mawlid provides an opportunity for Muslims to reflect on the role of the Prophet Muhammad in their own lives and in the world.

Important hashtags: #MawlidunNabi #mawlid #mawlidunnikah #milad #miladunnab #happybirthdayprophetmuhammad

LET'S UNLOCK

How can I add value to this community?

What activities could I plan to support this awareness day?

How can I show my support on social Media?

How can I continue the momentum?

September 20: HeForShe (Women)

What is it about?

Breaking the negative stereotype and challenges of women is not a woman's job alone because directly or not, It affects everyone. Both men and women.

That is why the HeForShe campaign was created by the UN Women to encourage men and boys around the world to take action in supporting women's rights. It was launched on September 20, 2014, by UN Women to end gender inequality globally.

Who does it impact?

The HeForShe campaign impacts everyone including men and women. The goal of the campaign is to engage men as agents of change to achieve gender equality.

Why is it important?

The HeForShe campaign is important as it engages men to join women in the struggle to achieve gender equality.

Important hashtags: #HeForShe #HeForSheDay #InternationalDayOfFeminism #GenderEquality

LET'S UNLOCK

How can I add value to this community?

```
```

What activities could I plan to support this awareness day?

```
```

How can I show my support on social Media?

```
```

How can I continue the momentum?

```
```

September 22: Autumnal Equinox

What is it about?

The Autumnal Equinox marks the beginning of fall. It occurs when the Sun crosses 180 degrees of celestial longitude, which is around September 22 in the Northern Hemisphere and March 20 in the Southern Hemisphere.

Who does it impact?

People from around the world, including visitors to specific locations during this time.

Why is it important?

The Autumnal Equinox marks the end of summer, which is a time for celebration with friends and loved ones. It is also a time to reflect on the good things in life and start new goals for the coming year.

Important hashtags: #AutumnEquinox #EndOfSummer

LET'S UNLOCK

How can I add value to this community?

What activities could I plan to support this awareness day?

How can I show my support on social Media?

How can I continue the momentum?

September 23: Bi Visbility Day (U.K.)

What is it about?

Bi Visibility Day is an annual LGBT awareness day that takes place on September 23rd to honour the bisexual community and raise awareness of bisexuality, gender identity and sexual orientation.

Who does it impact?

People from all over the world who identify as bisexual or otherwise.

Why is it important?

Bi Visibility Day is important because it raises awareness of the life experiences of bisexual people and the challenges they can face, both socially and in politics.

Important hashtags: #BiVisibilityDay #bipride #bisolidarity #biexistence

LET'S UNLOCK

How can I add value to this community?

What activities could I plan to support this awareness day?

How can I show my support on social Media?

How can I continue the momentum?

September 30 - October 6: National Inclusion Week

What is it about?

National inclusion week is a week to celebrate inclusion at every aspect of society.

As we all know, diversity is important. However, diversity without inclusion is of no essence. That is why this week is dedicated to encouraging inclusion of all diversities into society.

Who does it impact?

People who are interested in diversity and inclusion.

Why is it important?

The power of diversity is only felt with inclusion. National Inclusion Week is a time to remind us of the importance and impact of inclusion at work and society in general.

Important Hashtags #DiversityandInclusion #NationalInclusionWeekU

LET'S UNLOCK

How can I add value to this community?

What activities could I plan to support this awareness day?

How can I show my support on social Media?

How can I continue the momentum?

October 2024

Sunday	Monday	Tuesday	Wednesday	Thursday	Friday	Saturday
29	30	1 Jerry Rescue Day	2 To mark the day Thurgood Marshall was sworn into the Supreme Court	3 To mark the date Frank Robinson was signed as Major League Manager	4	5
			October 2-4: Rosh Hashanah (Jewish) (U.K.)			
6 **International Lesbian Day World Cerebral Palsy Day	7	8 ((World Dyslexia Awareness Day	9 **Coming Out Day (U.K.) Baby Loss Awareness Week	10 **World Sight Day World Mental Health Day	11	12 Yum Kippur
13	14 **Indigenous People Day (U.S.) Black Entrepreneur's Day	15 **International Day of Rural Women	16	17 Black Poetry Day Spirit Day	18 World Menopause Day ((?I rgQj_t cpw B_w	19 (LGBTQ+) **International Npml msl q B_w
20	21	22 ** Stuttering Awareness Day	23 Shemini Atzeret	24	25	26 **Intersex Awareness Day
27	28	29 **World Stroke Day	30	31 Diwali (Hinduism)	1	2

October: Global Diversity Awareness Month	** ADHD Awareness Month
National Disability Employment Awareness Month (NDEMAM)	**Bullying Prevention Month
Breast Cancer Awareness Month	**Awareness days or month not included in overview
Black History Month (U.K.)	

October

October 3-4: Rosh Hashanah (Jewish) (U.K.)

What is it about?

Rosh Hashanah, also known as the Jewish New Year, is a holiday that commemorates the judgment day of God.

Who does it impact?

Jews around the world, or those who have recently converted to Judaism.

Why is it important?

It's important because observing this holiday can help people reflect on their lives and how they are living them. It also provides a chance to thank God for the good things in their lives, and ask for more blessings.

Important hashtags: #RoshHashanah #JewishNewYear #Jews

LET'S UNLOCK

How can I add value to this community?

[blank box]

What activities could I plan to support this awareness day?

[blank box]

How can I show my support on social Media?

[blank box]

How can I continue the momentum?

[blank box]

October

October: Global Diversity Awareness Month

What is it about?

Global Diversity Awareness Month is a time to celebrate our various differences.

It's a time to embrace our diversities and realize that our differences don't separate us. They only make each of us unique in different ways. Also, diversity gives us different perspectives and a broader view of life we may have been missing out on.

Global diversity awareness day was created in 2006 by Worldwide Speakers Bureau (now The Speakers Bureau Group) and was adopted by UNESCO in 2007. October is the focus month because it is the month of the Kala Utsav, or "Monsoon".

Who does it impact?

People from all over the world, especially those who are immigrants to a new country.

Why is it important?

It's important because the world is home to many different kinds of people, and all kinds of people are needed for a healthy and successful society. Also, diversity can be a source of new ideas and solutions.

Important hashtags: #GlobalDiversityAwarenessMonth #DiversityMatters #DiversityInAction #KalaUtsav

LET'S UNLOCK

How can I add value to this community?

What activities could I plan to support this awareness day?

How can I show my support on social Media?

How can I continue the momentum?

October: National Disability Employment Awareness Month (NDEMAM)

What is it about?

National Disability Employment Awareness Month celebrates the contributions of the nation's job seekers with disabilities. It was established by The WorkPlace Fairness Act of 2001, which makes it an obligation for employers to comply with certain employment standards.

Who does it impact?

Job seekers with disabilities and their families, but also employers and their employees.

Why is it important?

NDEMAM is important because it encourages employers to hire qualified employees with disabilities, instead of discriminating against them. It also helps create awareness about the skills and talents of job seekers with disabilities. Importantly, it sends the message that people who have a disability are valuable members of society.

Important hashtags: #NDEMAM #DisabilityEmployment #Disability

LET'S UNLOCK

How can I add value to this community?

What activities could I plan to support this awareness day?

How can I show my support on social Media?

How can I continue the momentum?

October: Breast Cancer Awareness Month

What is it about?

With 7.8 million women diagnosed with breast cancer at the end of 2020, Breast cancer is now the most prevalent cancer.

It is imperative that we create the awareness for early diagnosis and treatment in order not to fall victim to this terrible disease.

October is Breast Cancer Awareness Month. Historically, awareness has been associated with the colour pink. This is the time to spread the word about everything concerning Breast Cancer.

Who does it impact?

People around the world are concerned about Breast Cancer.

Why is it important?

Breast cancer is the most common cancer in women, and occurs when abnormal cells begin to grow uncontrollably. Early detection of breast cancer can save lives, which makes it important to spread awareness about the disease and how to prevent it.

Important hashtags: #BreastCancerAwarenessMonth #PinkOctober

LET'S UNLOCK

How can I add value to this community?

What activities could I plan to support this awareness day?

How can I show my support on social Media?

How can I continue the momentum?

October: Black History Month (U.K.)

What is it about?

Black history is a fundamental part of the black race.
Though it's not pretty, it must be told so we do not forget black roots
and heritage.

The month of October is meant for reflecting on our history and to give
honour to the heroes who fought against the challenges of black people.

Who does it impact?

People from all around the world, particularly people from the UK.

Why is it important?

Black History Month is important because it highlights Black culture and
achievements throughout history. It also helps people create a sense of
belonging and acceptance of individuals from other cultures.

Important hashtags: #BlackHistoryMonth #TheProudRace
#BlackLivesMatter

LET'S UNLOCK

How can I add value to this community?

What activities could I plan to support this awareness day?

How can I show my support on social Media?

How can I continue the momentum?

October 1: Jerry Rescue Day

What is it about?

During the dark times of American history, a slave popularly called Jerry made a name for himself when he successfully escaped after he was arrested the same day in Syracuse, New York.

Who does it impact?

People of colour

Why is it important?

This day is important because it reminds us of the strength and resilience of people of colour. It also reminds us that we have always been fighting for our freedom and that we will continue to fight for our rights.

Important hastags: #JerryRescueDay #BlackFreedomFighters #JerryRescue #AfricanAmericanHistory

LET'S UNLOCK

How can I add value to this community?

What activities could I plan to support this awareness day?

How can I show my support on social Media?

How can I continue the momentum?

October 2: To mark the day Thurgood Marshall was sworn into the Supreme Court

What is it about?

A day to celebrate the life and legacy of Thurgood Marshall, a lawyer who became the first African American Supreme Court Justice.

Who does it impact?

People who practice American Law and those who want to learn more about his life and history.

Why is it important?

Thurgood Marshall was a very influential figure in American history and should be celebrated for his impact on society. He was the first African American Supreme Court Justice and helped change America's laws around equality and justice.

Important hashtags: #ThurgoodMarshallDay

LET'S UNLOCK

How can I add value to this community?

What activities could I plan to support this awareness day?

How can I show my support on social Media?

How can I continue the momentum?

October 3: To mark the date Frank Robinson was signed as Major League Manager

What is it about?

Frank Robinson is a former major league player who became the first major league manager on October 3, 1975. He is considered to be one of the greatest players in major league baseball and October 3 is a day to celebrate his life and legacy.

Who does it impact?

Fans of American Baseball and those who want to learn more about his life, career, and impact on the sport.

Why is it important?

Robinson was a very influential baseball player who changed history in his time on the field. He was the first African American manager in Major League Baseball and broke so many barriers for race relations in America, paving the way for future generations to come.

Important hashtags: #FrankRobinsonDay #FrankRobinson #MajorLeagueManager #baseball #Ballplayer #Manager #MajorLeague

LET'S UNLOCK

How can I add value to this community?

What activities could I plan to support this awareness day?

How can I show my support on social Media?

How can I continue the momentum?

October 6: World Cerebral Palsy Day

What is it about?

Cerebral palsy is a disability that affects movement and balancing. World Cerebral Palsy Day was established in 2004 by the World Federation of Cerebral Palsy Associations (WFCPA) to raise awareness of cerebral palsy.

Who does it impact?

People from all over the world who have an awareness of cerebral palsy. This includes individuals, as well as organizations that support people with cerebral palsy.

Why is it important?

World Cerebral Palsy Day is important because it aims to raise awareness of how people with cerebral palsy can lead fulfilling lives and overcome the obstacles cerebral palsy causes.

LET'S UNLOCK

How can I add value to this community?

What activities could I plan to support this awareness day?

How can I show my support on social Media?

How can I continue the momentum?

October 9-15: Baby Loss Awareness Week

What is it about?

This is a time to support anyone who has suffered pregnancy loss at any time. During this week, families are encouraged and the public is made aware of factors that may lead to a baby loss and how to prevent it.

Who does it impact?

People affected by pregnancy and baby loss.

Why is it important?

To create awareness of forums available to anyone affected by pregnancy and baby loss and assure that they are not alone.

Important hashtags: #PregnancyLoss #Miscarriage #InfantLoss

LET'S UNLOCK

How can I add value to this community?

What activities could I plan to support this awareness day?

How can I show my support on social Media?

How can I continue the momentum?

October 10: World Mental Health Day

What is it about?

World Mental Health Day was created to commemorate the 1984 International World Conference on Mental Health. It was first observed in 1999 and focuses mainly on mental illness around the world.

Who does it impact?

People around the world with mental health concerns, such as depression and anxiety disorders.

Why is it important?

Mental illness can be a burden for anyone, but particularly for people who are struggling with many problems at once. Mental illness is a serious health concern, and a large percentage of mental illnesses can be treated through psychological therapy.

Important hashtags: #WorldMentalHealthDay #MentalHealth

LET'S UNLOCK

How can I add value to this community?

What activities could I plan to support this awareness day?

How can I show my support on social Media?

How can I continue the momentum?

October 12: Yum Kippur

What is it about?

Yom Kippur is observed by Jews all around the world, and takes place on the 10th day of Tishrei. It is considered to be the holiest day in the Jewish calendar. It follows a 25-hour fast where no eating or drinking is allowed.

Who does it impact?

People of Jewish faith and those who observe Yom Kippur.

Why is it important?

Yom Kippur serves as a reminder to be grateful for the good in our lives and to forgive others. It also allows an opportunity for reflection and the ability to change our behaviour.

Important hashtags: #YomKippur #WorldJewishDay

LET'S UNLOCK

How can I add value to this community?

What activities could I plan to support this awareness day?

How can I show my support on social Media?

How can I continue the momentum?

October 14: Black Entrepreneur's Day

What is it about?

From Daymond John to Sean Combs to Oprah Winfrey, Black entrepreneurs all over the world have excelled in different fields and this day is meant to celebrate the business success and accomplishments of African Americans who lead in business.

Who does it impact?

People worldwide, particularly people of African descent.

Why is it important?

The success of many successful African Americans can be traced back to a strong community network, and this is especially true for those in the business world. This day is a way of showing how important this is, and how successful African Americans can influence others through business.

Important hashtags: #BlackEntrepreneursDay #blackentrepreneurs #blackbusiness #blackeconomics #blackjobs

LET'S UNLOCK

How can I add value to this community?

What activities could I plan to support this awareness day?

How can I show my support on social Media?

How can I continue the momentum?

October 17: Black Poetry Day

What is it about?

A day to celebrate poetry written by Afro-Americans and works on the subject of race. It is also a time to commemorate the birth of the first published black poet in the United States, Jupiter Hammon.

Who does it impact?

People who are interested in African American poetry and those who love to write poetry.

Why is it important?

Black poetry has a long history and is a part of many people's hearts, minds, and lives. It should be celebrated for its beauty.

Important hashtags: #BlackPoetryDay #BPoetry #PoetryIsNotDead #SpokenWord

LET'S UNLOCK

How can I add value to this community?

What activities could I plan to support this awareness day?

How can I show my support on social Media?

How can I continue the momentum?

October 18: World Menopause Day

What is it about?

Menopause is a natural decline in the production of reproductive hormones in women as they age and a number of women struggle with the challenges when it sets in.

This day is dedicated to raising awareness of menopause and the support options available to improve health and wellbeing.

Who does it impact?

It impacts women usually between the ages of 45 and 55 years old.

Why is it important?

It is important to raise awareness and engage various communities to educate individuals around the world.

Important hashtags: #MenopauseRelief #MenopauseSupport #MenopauseWeightloss

LET'S UNLOCK

How can I add value to this community?

What activities could I plan to support this awareness day?

How can I show my support on social Media?

How can I continue the momentum?

October 17: Spirit Day (LGBTQ+)

What is it about?

Spirit day is a day that people support the LGBT+ community to embrace their identity and condemn bullying. People who participate mostly wear purple in solidarity.

Who does it impact?

People around the world who are associated with LGBTQ+, such as parents, siblings, friends and relatives. Everyone should be free to live their lives as they choose, without fear or offence from others.

Why is it important?

Spirit Day is important because it sends the message that people should never be judged or bullied based on their identity. The LGBTQ+ community faces a great deal of prejudice and discrimination, which is why Spirit Day is important to help fight those stereotypes.

Important hashtags: #SpiritDay #LGBTQ

LET'S UNLOCK

How can I add value to this community?

What activities could I plan to support this awareness day?

How can I show my support on social Media?

How can I continue the momentum?

October 23: Shemini Atzeret

What is it about?

Shemini Atzeret is a holiday that occurs on the eighth day after the seven-day holiday of Sukkot. It is a time to reflect on the past year and to give thanks for the bounty of the harvest.

Who does it impact?

Shemini Atzeret is a Jewish holiday that impacts people of the Jewish faith.

Why is it important?

The Shemini Atzeret holiday is important because it is the final day of the Sukkot festival. It is also a time to reflect on the past year and make resolutions for the coming year.

Important hashtags: #SheminiAtzere #sukkot #simchatTorah

LET'S UNLOCK

How can I add value to this community?

What activities could I plan to support this awareness day?

How can I show my support on social Media?

How can I continue the momentum?

October 31: Diwali (Hinduism)

What is it about?

Diwali is the most significant day in the Hindu calendar. It marks the time of the autumn harvest and is celebrated with various religious festivities of light and fire.

Who does it impact?

Celebrated by many people around the world, particularly within the Hindu faith.

Why is it important?

The significance of Diwali lies in its celebration of life and family. Diwali also celebrates the triumph of good over evil, hope over despair and prosperity over poverty. The day symbolizes the endless cycle of life and death and the transition between this world and the next.

Important hashtags: #Diwali #Hinduism

LET'S UNLOCK

How can I add value to this community?

What activities could I plan to support this awareness day?

How can I show my support on social Media?

How can I continue the momentum?

November 2024

Sunday	Monday	Tuesday	Wednesday	Thursday	Friday	Saturday
27	28	29	30	31	1 All Saints' Day **Bandi Chhor Divas (Sikh)	2 **Anniversary of the Crowning of Haile Selassie (Rastafari)
3	4	5	6	7	8	9 **Intersex Day of Solidarity **World Freedom Day **World Adoption Day
10 **Remembrance Sunday	11 **Armistice Day	12	13 **World Kindness Day	14 **World Diabetes Day	15 **Birthday of Guru Nanak Dev (Sikh)	16 Disability History Month (U.K.)
17	18 LGBT STEM Day (U.K.)	19 **International Men's Day	20 Transgender Day of Remembrance (LGBTQ+) (U.K.	21	22	23 **Survivors of Suicide Loss Day
24 Umoja Karamu Celebration	25 **International Day for the Elimination of Violence Against Women	26 **Ascension of Abdu'l-Bahá (Baha'i)	27	28 **Thanks Giving	29	30 **St. Andrews Day

November 13-17: National Anti-Bullying Week (U.K.)

** Pancreatic Cancer Awareness Month

** Islamophobia Awareness Month

**Awareness Day or Month not included in the overview

**Movember

**National Family Caregivers Month

Diversity and Inclusion Unlocked ™ Planner

November

November 1: All Saints' Day

What is it about?

All Saints Day is a christian celebration to commemorate Christians who have attained spiritual maturity known as Saints.

Who does it impact?

People of the Christian faith in observance of All Saints' Day. They also impact people who have friends or family members who observe this holiday.

Why is it important?

All Saints' Day recognizes the importance of death and the love and relationships we have with others who have passed on. It is a time to remember those we have lost, but also a reminder to be grateful for what we do have.

Important hashtags: AllSaintsDay, #AllSoulsDay, # Saints, and #Catholic

LET'S UNLOCK

How can I add value to this community?

What activities could I plan to support this awareness day?

How can I show my support on social Media?

How can I continue the momentum?

The 4th Sunday in November: Umoja Karamu Celebration

What is it about?

Umoja Karamu is a swahili word meaning unity feast. The celebration is aimed at instilling solidarity, black values, and appreciation of black heritage into black families. The celebration begun in 1971 by Dr. Edward Sims.

Who does it impact?

African Americans and people who are interested in or love African culture

Why is it important?

Umoja Karamu is a way of celebrating diversity among the world's cultures and societies. It is a celebration that highlights some of the beautiful, skilled, and culturally-important aspects of African peoples' cultures, while also celebrating their strengths as individuals.

Important hashtags: #UmojaKaramu #AfricanAmericanUnity #karamu, #umoja, #blackhistory #culture

LET'S UNLOCK

How can I add value to this community?

What activities could I plan to support this awareness day?

How can I show my support on social Media?

How can I continue the momentum?

November 13-17: National Anti-Bullying Week (U.K.)

What is it about?

From teachers to parents and influences to politicians, we all have a role to play in ending bullying. Depression, pain, sadness, hopelessness. These are some of the negative feelings that bullying has on people.

This anti bullying week, reach out to someone who you feel is being bullied and if you are being bulled reach out to someone you trust as soon as possible.

Who does it impact?

People from all over who are involved with or affected by bullying or a school environment that promotes bullying.

Why is it important?

National Anti-Bullying Week is important because it raises awareness of the serious effects bullying has on society. It also provides information and advice on how to prevent bullying and provide support for those who have been affected by it.

Important hashtags: #StopBullying, #NoBully, #RUAWN

LET'S UNLOCK

How can I add value to this community?

What activities could I plan to support this awareness day?

How can I show my support on social Media?

How can I continue the momentum?

November 16: Disability History Month (U.K.)

What is it about?

Disability History Month aims to raise awareness of the historical, social and cultural factors that have made people with disabilities, who are mainstreamed into society, and the issues that remain for marginalized groups.

Who does it impact?

People from all over the world who are associated with or affected by people with disabilities.

Why is it important?

Disability History Month is important because it raises awareness of the social, political and cultural history that has affected people with disabilities, as well as their ability to live in contemporary society.
I
mportant hastags: #DisabilityHistoryMonth, #DHM, #DisableTheHate, #SpreadTheWord, #EndTheStigma

LET'S UNLOCK

How can I add value to this community?

```



```

What activities could I plan to support this awareness day?

```



```

How can I show my support on social Media?

```



```

How can I continue the momentum?

```



```

November 18: LGBTSTEM Day (U.K.)

What is it about?

LGBTSTEM Day is an international day celebrating the contributions of members of the LGBT community to science, technology, engineering and math (STEM) fields.

Who does it impact?

People from all over who are scientists or engineers in the workplace.

Why is it important?

LGBTSTEM Day is important because it raises awareness of the importance of education and encourages young LGBT people to value their scientific achievements.

Important hastags: #LGBTSTEM #RainbowSTEM #PrideinSTEM #LGBTinSTEM #STEMforLGBT

LET'S UNLOCK

How can I add value to this community?

What activities could I plan to support this awareness day?

How can I show my support on social Media?

How can I continue the momentum?

November 20: Transgender Day of Remembrance (LGBTQ+) (U.K.)

What is it about?

2021 was a deadly year for trans people with 46 lives lost due to discrimination, especially trans people of colour. Moving forward we must remember that trans lives matter too.

The Transgender Day of Remembrance was first observed in 1999 and created by Gwendolyn Ann Smith to honour those who were killed because of their gender identity.

Who does it impact?

Allies and members of the LGBTQ+ community, especially transgender people.

Why is it important?

The significance of Transgender Day of Remembrance lies in its recognition and celebration of transgender people. Transgender people face a lot of discrimination, and it's important to remember that not all members of the community are victims. The day is also a reminder that violence, hatred, and prejudice should never be encouraged.

Important hashtags: #TransgenderDayOfRememberance #Trans #TDOR #RememberOurDead

LET'S UNLOCK

How can I add value to this community?

What activities could I plan to support this awareness day?

How can I show my support on social Media?

How can I continue the momentum?

December 2024

Sunday	Monday	Tuesday	Wednesday	Thursday	Friday	Saturday
1 World Aids Day Rosa Parks Day	2 The International Day for the Abolition of Slavery	3 International Day of Persons With Disability	4	5	6	7
8 **Rohatsu (Bodhi Day) (Buddhist)	9	10 Human Rights Day	11	12 **International Universal Health Coverage Day	13	14
15	16	17	18	19	20 ** International Human Solidarity Day	21
22	23 ** International Migrant's Day	24 **Christmas Eve (Christian)	25 Christmas (Christian) Hanukkah (Jewish)	26 **Chanukah begins (Judaism) **Saint Stephen's Day (Christian)	27	28
29	30	31	1	2	3	4
31	1	2	3	4	5	6

December 26-January 1: Kwanzaa (U.S.)

** Universal Human Rights Month

** HIV/AIDS Awareness Month

**Awareness Day or Month not included in the overview

December

December 1: World Aids Day

What is it about?

After more than 40 years, the world is still plagued with a highly infectious threat, HIV/AIDS. As at 2020, there were approximaely 38 million people across the globe living with HIV. Although, the world has made progress in handling the disease since its inception, there's still much work to be done.

The 1st of December is a day to raise awareness about the HIV/AIDS epidemic and how to reduce it's spread.

Who does it impact?

People from around the world who are concerned about AIDS and HIV, especially those in Africa, South America and other developing countries.

Why is it important?

As at 2020, approximately 38 million people were living with HIV. It's also important to remember that there are many different types of people living with HIV, and there are ways to prevent getting it.

Important hashtags: #WorldAidsDay #HIV

LET'S UNLOCK

How can I add value to this community?

What activities could I plan to support this awareness day?

How can I show my support on social Media?

How can I continue the momentum?

December 1: Rosa Parks Day

What is it about?

Picture this. You get on a bus. Pay your fare and pick a comfortable seat for yourself. Then suddenly, the driver tells you to vacate your seat for someone else because of the colour of your skin. What do you do?

This scenario played out in a Montgomery bus in 1943 when the bus driver ordered Rosa Parks was told to vacate her seat for other white people when the white section of the bus was full. Parks rejected the driver's order and was eventually arrested for that.

However, she went on to be honoured by the United Congress as "the first lady of civil rights" and "the mother of the freedom movement"

In Ohio and Oregon, December 1 is a day dedicated to remembering her bravery and efforts towards fighting racial segregation.

Who does it impact?

It is celebrated by people of colour and anyone who values equality, justice, and dignity.

Why is it important?

By encouraging students and staff to become more aware of their own cultural heritage and the diversity of our nation, school districts can build bridges between themselves and other communities.

Important hashtags: #RosaParksDay #CivilRights #RosaParks

LET'S UNLOCK

How can I add value to this community?

[ ]

What activities could I plan to support this awareness day?

[ ]

How can I show my support on social Media?

[ ]

How can I continue the momentum?

[ ]

December 2: The International Day for the Abolition of Slavery

What is it about?

A day to celebrate the lives of all slaves and all the abolitionists who fought against slavery.

Who does it impact?

People who were affected by slavery or are interested in the cause of ending slavery.

Why is it important?

Slavery is wrong and should be ended everywhere. It has always been a brutal, inhumane practice that only ended with the Civil War. Celebrating the abolition of slavery and fighting for its end is a way of showing that it still exists today, and needs to be ended.

Imortant hashtags: #AbolishSlavery, #AbolishSlaveTrade #EndHumanTrafficking #Slavery #HumanTrafficking # trafficking

LET'S UNLOCK

How can I add value to this community?

What activities could I plan to support this awareness day?

How can I show my support on social Media?

How can I continue the momentum?

December 3: International Day of Persons With Disability

What is it about?

There are at least 1 billion people living with a disability. It's important we are well educated about the various forms of disabilities and their challenges.

December 3 is a time to remember that not all disabilities are visible and to create awareness about the special needs for the various disabilities.

Who does it impact?

People from around the world raising awareness or acquiring knowledge about mental and physical disabilities.

Why is it important?

It's important because over 350 million people are living with a disability, and 20% of those live in developing countries. People with disabilities face a lot of discrimination and social ostracization, which is why the International Day of Persons With Disabilities is important to help fight that prejudice.

Important hashtags: #InternationalDayOfPersonsWithDisabilities #Disability

LET'S UNLOCK

How can I add value to this community?

What activities could I plan to support this awareness day?

How can I show my support on social Media?

How can I continue the momentum?

December 25: Hanukkah (Jewish)

What is it about?

Hanukkah means "dedication" in Hebrew, and celebrates the rededication of a family's home. Hanukkah is observed during the eight days starting on the 25th day of Kislev.

Who does it impact?

People from around the world who are identified as Jewish, or by those who share their faith.

Why is it important?

The significance of Hanukkah lies in its celebration of light and life. It's important to remember that freedom, love and peace should never be taken for granted.

Important hashtags: #Hanukkah #Jewish

LET'S UNLOCK

How can I add value to this community?

```



```

What activities could I plan to support this awareness day?

```



```

How can I show my support on social Media?

```



```

How can I continue the momentum?

```



```

December 10: Human Rights Day

What is it about?

Human Rights day is a day dedicated to celebrating the proclamation of the Universal Declaration of Human Rights by the United Nations on 10 December, 1948.

Who does it impact?

Everyone

Why is it important?

It's important to recognize the rights we all have as humans.

Important hashtags #Humanrights

LET'S UNLOCK

How can I add value to this community?

What activities could I plan to support this awareness day?

How can I show my support on social Media?

How can I continue the momentum?

December 25: Christmas (Christian)

What is it about?

The birth of Jesus is one of the most significant events in the bible. Asides the supernatural birth by a virgin, his birth was prophesied by prophets hundred of years before he was born.

Christmas is annually celebrated mostly on December 25. It's also celebrated on the 24th in some parts of the world like Brazil, poland, Czech Republic, Poland, Germany.

Who does it impact?

People from around the world who are associated with Christianity, especially Christians around the world.

Why is it important?

The significance of Christmas lies in its celebration of life. Christmas Day is a time to reflect on the things that are most important to us, like family and community.

Important hashtags: #Christmas #Christian #birthofchrist

LET'S UNLOCK

How can I add value to this community?

[ ]

What activities could I plan to support this awareness day?

[ ]

How can I show my support on social Media?

[ ]

How can I continue the momentum?

[ ]

December 26-January 1: Kwanzaa (U.S.)

What is it about?

Kwanzaa is a celebration of African heritage for people of African descent in America. The celebration was established by Dr. Maluana Karenga in 1966.The purpose of the celebration was to reaffirm and restore the rootness of Africans and African Americans in African culture.

Who does it impact?

People who are interested in, or love, the positive aspects of being African and/or African American.

Why is it important?

Kwanzaa is a celebration of the positive things that come from being African, and that there are many ways to be black that are beautiful. Kwanza has a history going back to 1966 and has continued to grow as a symbol of pride in being black.

Important hashtags: #Kwanzaa #HappyKwanzaa #KwanzaaCelebration #FirstFruits #SevenPrinciples #AfricanAmerican

LET'S UNLOCK

How can I add value to this community?

```
```

What activities could I plan to support this awareness day?

```
```

How can I show my support on social Media?

```
```

How can I continue the momentum?

```
```

Are you ready for the next step in your Diversity and Inclusion journey?

Are you looking to make a change in your business and want to learn from the biggest names in the industry?

Do you want your company to be as diverse and inclusive as possible, but you don't know where to start?

It can feel like a daunting task trying to identify the diversity and inclusion gaps in your organisation or company
Many businesses don't even know where to start when it comes to diversity and inclusion, let alone make any real progress.   FACTS

There are so many things to consider, from attracting and retaining diverse talent and customers, to how you market to different groups of people and have the confidence to say the right thing!

That's where our Diversity and Inclusion personalised FREE quiz comes in.

Just scan this QR to start your next step

This FREE quiz will help you access and evaluate your current business operation to see how up-to-date you are when it comes to implementing diversity and inclusion in your organization.

Learn how the top global companies are addressing Diversity and Inclusion across their organisation so you can leap years ahead and do so too!

According to some interesting findings:

Organisations identified as more diverse and inclusive are 35% more likely to outperform their competitors. (McKinsey)
Diverse companies are 70% more likely to capture new markets. (HBR)
Diverse teams are 87% better at making decisions. (People Management)
Diverse management teams lead to 19% higher revenue. (BCG)

It's an exciting time and it can only get better and better with our diversity and inclusion expertise Unlocked in your business

A little statistic:

The Black Pound Report 2022 reveals the untapped economic power of the UK's Multi-Ethnic consumers goes into 4.5 billion missed opportunities and it's simply that consumers are more likely to purchase a service or product if they see the representation of inclusion in your business

Your organisation cannot afford to be left behind.

You need to be on the right side of history as you work towards growing your business and improving profitable outcomes.

Simply take this three-minute quiz to unravel the best-kept industry secrets to tapping into billions by doing the right thing for the right reasons.

Take the diversity and inclusion quiz now and begin your business transformation for growth and success!

Also do not forget to follow me on LinkedIn

Printed in Great Britain
by Amazon

32383230R00145